MW00573807

In Defiance of Oppression
The Legacy of Boudicca

a Girl God Anthology

Edited by Trista Hendren,
Joey Morris
and Pat Daly

Preface by Jaclyn Cherie

Cover Art by Molly Roberts

©2021 All Rights Reserved
ISBN: 978-82-93725-20-6

*All writings and art are the property of individual contributors.
All rights reserved. None of the writings or artwork herein may be
reproduced or utilized in any form or by any means, electronic
or mechanical, including photocopying, recording or by any information
storage and retrieval system, without prior written permission
from the author or artist.*

www.thegirlgod.com

Girl God Books

Warrior Queen: Answering the Call of The Morrigan

Warrior Queen: Answering the Call of The Morrigan is a powerful anthology about the Irish Celtic Goddess. Each contributor brings The Morrigan to life with unique stories that invite readers to partake and inspire them to pen their own. Included are essays, poems, stories, chants, rituals, and art from dozens of story-tellers and artists from around the world, illustrating and recounting the many ways this powerful Goddess of war, death, and prophecy has changed their lives.

Original Resistance: Reclaiming Lilith, Reclaiming Ourselves

There is, perhaps, no more powerful archetype of female resistance than Lilith. As women across the globe rise up against the patriarchy, Lilith stands beside them, misogyny's original challenger. This anthology—a chorus of voices hitting chords of defiance, liberation, anger and joy—reclaims the goodness of women bold enough to hold tight to their essence. Through poetry, prose, incantation, prayer and imagery, women from all walks of life invite you to join them in the revolutionary act of claiming their place—of reclaiming themselves.

Re-visioning Medusa: from Monster to Divine Wisdom

A remarkable collection of essays, poems, and art by scholars who have researched Her, artists who have envisioned Her, and women who have known Her in their personal story. All have spoken with Her and share something of their communion in this anthology.

Inanna's Ascent: Reclaiming Female Power

Inanna's Ascent examines how females can rise from the underworld and reclaim their power, sovereignly expressed through poetry, prose and visual art. All contributors are extraordinary women in their own right, who have been through some difficult life lessons—and are brave enough to share their stories.

On the Wings of Isis: Reclaiming the Sovereignty of Auset
For centuries, women have lived, fought and died for their equality, independence and sovereignty. Originally known as Auset, the Egyptian Goddess Isis reveals such a path. Unfurl your wings and join an array of strong women who have embodied the Goddess of Ten Thousand Names to celebrate their authentic selves.

New Love: a reprogramming toolbox for undoing the knots
A powerful combination of emotional/spiritual techniques, art and inspiring words for women who wish to move away from patriarchal thought. *New Love* includes a mixture of compelling thoughts and suggestions for each day, along with a "toolbox" to help you change the parts of your life you want to heal.

How to Live Well Despite Capitalist Patriarchy
A book challenging societal assumptions to help women become stronger and break free of their chains.

The Girl God
A book for children young and old, celebrating the Divine Female by Trista Hendren. Magically illustrated by Elisabeth Slettnes with quotes from various faith traditions and feminist thinkers.

Tell Me Why
A feminist twist of the creation story told with love from a mother to her son, in hopes of crafting a different world for them both. Written by Trista Hendren / Illustrated by Elisabeth Slettnes.

My Name is Medusa
The story of the greatly misunderstood Goddess, including why she likes snakes. *My Name is Medusa* explores the "scary" dark side, the potency of nature and the importance of dreams. Arna Baartz gorgeously illustrates this tale by Glenys Livingstone, teaching children (big and small) that our power often lies in what we have been taught to fear and revile.

Complete list of Girl God publications at www.thegirlgod.com

"May you never be subservient.
May you never fall prey to fitting in.
May you always swirl in all the directions
the sacred winds want to take you.
May you never hush your laughter nor your tears.
May you breathe without restriction.
May you show up every single day
to the calling that is you and
may you always know
the courage of your heart."

-Fig Ally (1960 - 2021)

Dedicated to the women and children of Afghanistan – and those around the world who continue to fight for their freedom.

Table of Contents

Preface: *Boudicca's Promise*   1
Jaclyn Cherie

Introduction   5
Joey Morris

A Note About Styles, Preferences and Names   9
Trista Hendren

Invocation to Boudicca   12
Joey Morris

Boudicea   13
Lisbeth Cheever-Gessaman

Define: Boudicca   14
Kay Louise Aldred

Battle Cry   15
Erika Lopp

Why We Need the Boudica Spirit Today   16
Sharon Smith

Warrior Queen   19
Barbara O' Meara

The Daughters of Boudicca   20
H. Byron Ballard

The Midwives   30
Lucy Pierce

Take Back Your Power   31
Rebekah Myers

We Rise
Melody Bergman

34

Warrior
Lucy Pierce

36

Warpaint – Mourning under Boudicca
Joey Morris

37

Shadow Work
Kathy Barenskie

40

The Importance of SHEroes
Trista Hendren

42

The Empowered Child
Jeanne Raines

46

Boudicca's Dream
Kaalii Cargill

47

Queen Boudicca
Molly Roberts

52

Rebellion and Reverence
Victoria Wilson-Randall

53

When The Colour Of Emotion Floods The Nervous System
Claire Dorey

54

Be Bold
Lady Wolf

65

Blind Spots (The Art of Survival)
Kathy Barenskie

66

Dreaming of Boudicca
Barbara O' Meara

68

The Audacious Spirit
Maureen Owen   69

Motherese
Lucy Pierce   80

Boudicca's Prayer on the Birth of Her First Daughter   81
Hayley Arrington

Defined by Our Defiance - Taking up Boudicca's Fight   82
Pandora Le Cora

Boudicca   95
Arlene Bailey

She Walks the Land Remembering   96
Arlene Bailey

Rage of a Woman   101
Arlene Bailey

Boudicca Rises   102
Arlene Bailey

O Sovereign Holy   108
Iris Eve

Boudicca   110
Andrea Redmond

The Story of Woman   111
Tamara Albanna

Boudicca and the Hare   113
Emma Clark

The Face of Defiance   114
Sionainn McLean

Defiance   118
Karen Storminger

Goddess Andraste   119
Joey Morris

Andraste   125
Kat Shaw

Lessons From Boudicca on the Spirit to Rebel from Within   126
Pamela Genghini Munoz

Is This the Best you Can Do?   132
Kay Louise Aldred

Reclamation of the Broken Spirit   134
Joey Morris

Supplication to Boudicca   138
Rebekah Myers

Boudicca Rising   140
Barbara O' Meara

Boudicca Speaks   141
Trista Hendren

List of Contributors   149

Acknowledgments   163

What's Next?   165

Boudicca's Promise

Preface by Jaclyn Cherie

"Nothing is safe from Roman pride and arrogance. They will deface the Sacred and will deflower our virgins. Win the battle or perish, that is what I, a Woman, will do."

-Bouddica's words of vengeance as recorded by Tacitus

I have had the honor of writing about some amazing Goddesses, and it is my hope with each Anthology released from the collective known as Girl God Books that the Divine Feminine will stir, awaken, and shine again, starting within the readers.

It is not often that these books tackle a Woman, an actual (once) living human being who embodies what it is to be a Goddess on Earth – defy the odds, topple the patriarchy, and lead a war that would quite literally go down in history while altering its course. Boudicca (Boudica, Boadicea) was a Celtic Queen who led a revolt against the Roman Ninth Legion.

For 17 years Boudicca and her Husband, King Prasutagus of the Iceni tribe ruled (A.D 43–A.D. 60) until his death where he left no male heir behind; only Boudicca and her two daughters.

The occupying forces took this opportunity of there being no ruler to confiscate all the riches, properties, and belongings of the late King who was once favored by the Romans. Boudicca was publicly flogged, and her daughters were raped by soldiers.[1]

Enraged by Roman occupation, fueled by loss and pain, Boudicca led an uprising with her fellow Britons who were also opposed to foreign rule.

---

1   Sarah Pruitt, History Channel

A slaughter ensued.

Boudicca and her army (comprised of Iceni and Trinovantes) defeated the Roman Ninth Legion in Camulodunum led by Gaius Suetonius Paulinus, after which she continued her massacre through London and Verulamium (modern day St. Albans).

Eventually, despite having more numbers and better odds, the Britons were defeated by the Roman Army. Boudicca and her daughters – facing certain torture and death – decided they would die how they lived: on their terms.

All 3 took poison and thus were not subjected to the fate that was scheduled to meet them.

They met death by their choice, and not that of any man.

Powerful as fuck.

This is not a Goddess by Divine birthright where we can analyze her archetype and/or worship across time and cultures then apply it to our lives or leave her story up to our own interpretation; this was a real Woman who lived, breathed, and bled just like you and me.

Though, I would personally argue that Boudicca is a Goddess; she earned that title by action, integrity, and the way she lived and died.

This story is important to tell because Women and Femmes all over the world are facing persecution, oppression and resistance from the systems meant to help us but built to work against us.

We are angry.

We are angry for ourselves.

We are angry for our Sisters.

We are angry for humanity.

The Divine Feminine is waking up and she is ready for war. We have passed the point where docile, meekness, batting our eyelashes, smiling, and nodding will get us anywhere. Did it ever really help us further the cause? Did Women's rights come from being quiet?

Or did it come from being loud? Making waves? Creating chaos? Femininity is a weapon 100% and it in fact has been weaponized to work against us – but Femininity doesn't always look like receptive energy; it takes many forms and one of them, the most powerful, is justified rage.

We are SCREAMING, ROARING, HOWLING.

We are reclaiming our bodies, reclaiming ourselves.

We are reclaiming our history and our future.

We are reclaiming our narrative.

We are reclaiming our power.

We are RISING against oppression in all forms.

We may not be going to war with the Roman Ninth Fleet, but we are going to war.

We are raging a war for income and housing equality, access to healthcare, basic human rights, autonomy, sovereignty and so much more.

We are fighting against patriarchy, misogyny, an unfair justice system and racism.

We are fighting back against harassment, and the male gaze.

I am not here to look pretty for you.

Women in general are not here to look pretty for you.

While we are at it, Women are not a rehab for broken men.

I said what I said.

Boudicca led an uprising to fight back against Roman occupation because there was no one else willing or able to do it. She took that role upon herself, knowing the risk.

I see the Spirit and Essence of Boudicca all around, pounding in the hearts and Souls of the Women and Femmes called to take up arms.

We have the numbers just like she did, except this time we will win the war.

Introduction

Joey Morris

Now, perhaps more than ever, I find myself turning to the fierce female warriors of the past for inspiration; those who found themselves facing seemingly insurmountable odds and choosing to fight for their freedom and liberations.

With political currents lending themselves to the suppression of women, seeking the driving back policies of bodily autonomy and civil liberties that would otherwise encourage fairness in our world, it is not difficult to feel under threat by the powers of Patriarchy.

It seeks to invade us – our countries, our ways of life, our bodies and even our minds; to bend and break women. To rule over us. We shall always resist.

Boudicca, the Celtic Queen of the Iceni tribe of Ancient Britannia, found herself and her daughters attacked, raped, and disinherited by the vehicle of Patriarchy that was the Roman Empire.
She chose to fight back.

In the ongoing aftermath of the political situation surrounding Doctor Ford and Kavanaugh, opinions and people were/are divided, battlelines were/are drawn, cries for basic human decency seemed to fall on deaf ears as female survivors were ridiculed, mocked and disbelieved on one side, with an outpouring of support and revealing of stories on the other.

I honour every survivor who speaks out.

Thank you for shining a light where it is needed, and to those who do not or cannot speak out; you are still heard, and loved.

As Women's civil liberties have been attacked in Poland, women there are in full rebellion. They are showing the power of Women who refuse to be dictated to by the state.

I honour every woman who puts herself on the picket line in order to find for justice, and a better tomorrow for all daughters.

These are just two examples in a sea of exploitation.

Women are attacked, sexually abused, shamed by the system of Patriarchy, and sought to be chained by their oppressors.

What seemed stark to me in the fallout of recent events was the response to shame and silence women, particularly by other women.

You somewhat expect the men who profit from holding women down to repeat their foul rhetoric; you know that they will fall on their outmoded swords and eventually we will bury them with that.

But to see women so indoctrinated that they throw other women down hoping for praise and scraps from this table is disturbing. I had been speaking on a separate personal issue that affected myself as another woman sought to discredit my work and mocked the fact that I was a sexual abuse survivor. (From this point on I will term this 'warrior' as I think survivor is not wholly better than victim and I do not like defining myself or those other warriors by the actions of their attackers.)

This came in the same political climate which saw other Warriors being shamed and I witnessed other women being triggered by her poison, and I could not let that pass.

Recent years have been a collection of uncomfortable truths, forcing us to sit in places within ourselves which are foreboding and inhospitable, so that we peer endlessly into the shadow of our being, and the shadows that plague other women indoctrinated by Patriarchy.

The path this year has been littered with learning... whether we like it or not.

As we see ourselves through complex and difficult scenarios, we glean insight into our true nature; what elevates us, what chains us, what washes us clean again.

Knowledge though, is beyond power, it is sacred, an ethereal cord to the wisdom of the universe, inviting us to sample the taste of the cosmos, taking a bite of infinity.

To share the knowledge and experience of Women is a great tool in the war for the liberation of all.

It can be awe inspiring and crushing at the same time, to feel both infinite and insignificant, to see our lessons and flaws laid bare and yet to know they are over in the blink of an eye.

Our lessons may be over quicker than we realise in this incarnation, but the legacy lives on, our actions, our words, have lasting impact.

We stand for change, and liberation.

We shall not be shamed or dominated.

As Boudicca called together the different Celtic tribes, so too shall we gather all the clans of Women and their allies from across the world.

As she resisted the overwhelming pressure from a corrupt society to bend to their will, so too shall we.

We shall invoke her complete refusal to be passive and accept a death by a thousand cuts.

We will not be dominated, nor oppressed, and we shall draw our battlelines.

We too will create a legacy of defiance in the face of oppression that will scream out across the ages, to be heard by our daughters and their daughters afterwards.

We are free creatures, and we will remain free.

A Note about Styles, Preferences and Names
Trista Hendren

In Defiance of Oppression contains a variety of writing styles from people around the world. Various forms of English are included in this anthology, and we chose to keep spellings of the writers' place of origin to honor/honour each individual's unique voice.

It was the expressed intent of the editors to not police standards of citation, transliteration, and formatting. Contributors have determined which citation style, italicization policy and transliteration system to adopt in their pieces. The resulting diversity reflects the diversity of academic fields, genres and personal expressions represented by the authors.[2]

Mary Daly wrote long ago that, "Women have had the power of naming stolen from us."[3] The quest for our own naming, and our own language, is never-ending, and each of us attempts it differently.

The editors wish to note that Boudicca is known by a variety of titles and spellings—as well as being associated with several Goddesses. We chose not to police how contributors addressed Her. As Vanessa Collingridge states in her biography:

> "Boudica... branded her legacy into the British psyche to the extent that almost two thousand years on, we are using her name as a byword for strong women leaders, fictional characters – even as the epitome of the nationalist or Celtic patriot. Dramatically, she is cast as

---

2 This paragraph is borrowed and adapted with love from *A Jihad for Justice: Honoring the Work and Life of Amina Wadud*. Edited by Kecia Ali, Juliane Hammer and Laury Silvers.

3 Daly, Mary. *Gyn/Ecology: The Metaethics of Radical Feminism*. Beacon Press, 1990.

another Braveheart, rolled back in time and space to the lands of East Anglia and the time of the Roman conquests; in reality, Boudica was a collaborator turned rebel and then infamous warrior queen. But until recently, for someone with such a tight grip on the British imagination, we've known very little about the real woman from antiquity; in fact, we still don't even know her real name. We grew up calling her "Boadicea" which turns out to have been an early gaffe after a scribe mistook her name in Latin and transposed two vital letters; however, it sounded right so it stuck for centuries until we realised the mistake. Over the past few years, she's been correctly renamed "Boudica" from the Celtic word "bouda" or "victory"; it's a chorus that was allegedly chanted again and again before warriors went into battle – but we still cannot even say for sure whether this was her real name or just a title. Boadicea, Bonduca, Boudicca or Boudica, she's a figure who has not only been cherished from our past but one who has been continually reinvented to serve as a "woman of our age". Such is her draw that whenever there has been a strong or high-profile woman in power (whether politically, economically, or in any other field), Boudica has been the reference point or role model in both words and pictures."[4]

I tend to spell her name Boudicca but that is just how I initially saw her name and that is what is in my head. I still can't say her name in a proper British intonation. My mother tells me it is something like Boo-dica, but I will probably continue to botch her name, as pronunciation has never been my strong point.

People often get caught up on whether we say *Goddess* or *Girl God* or *Divine Female* vs. *Divine Feminine*. Personally, I try to just listen to what the speaker is trying to say. The fact remains that few of us were privileged with a woman-affirming education—and

---

4   Collingridge, Vanessa. *Boudica: A Groundbreaking Biography of the True Warrior Queen*, Ebury, 2006.

we all have a lot of time to make up for. Let's all be gentle with each other through that process.

If you find that a particular writing doesn't sit well with you, please feel free to use the Al-Anon suggestion: "Take what you like, leave the rest!" That said, if there aren't at least several pieces that challenge you, we have not done our job here.

For those who take issue with Boudicca's violent legacy, I leave you these words from Malcolm X.

> "Concerning non-violence: it is criminal to teach people not to defend themselves when they are the victims of constant brutal attacks."

May we, and our daughters, find strength and protection—and may we create a world that is safe for *all* women and children.

Invocation to Boudicca

Joey Morris

"I speak now to Boudicca
Ancient Queen of the Iceni
I call forward from the depths of time
Your ferocity of conviction
Lend me your strength,
To never cower in the face of oppression,
Instead to bare my teeth and woad my brow.
Let them underestimate us
We will make them bleed for their hubris
And count this mistake amongst the fallen
Boudicca

Ancient Queen of the Iceni
Who saw the travesties of an invading force
Whose designs were domination
To break the backs and wills of others
And knowing this,
Broke their vanity
To teach them the meaning of fear
Boudicca

Ancient Queen of the Iceni
Keep me resilient when my heart quakes
And aches from the dispassionate cruelty of others
Help me raise a spear far above my head
And howl a battle cry so frenzied
That all those who seek to tether me
Will know trepidation."

Boudicea
Lisbeth Cheever-Gessaman

Define: Boudicca

Kay Louise Aldred

Great British Queen, Change Maker, Warrioress.

Defender of Home.

Self-Directive, Non-Compliant, Autonomous.

Model of Agency.

Righteously Rageful, Vindicated Vengeance, Fearless.

Embodiment of Fury.

Extinct archetype ready to be revived.

Battle Cry
Erika Lopp

Twas a time long ago when the Great Isle was ravished with war and bloodshed. Invaders from the east swept through the land intent on domination.

Amidst these trying times rose a warrior. Boudicca, a name still whispered in the echoes of time. Boudicca the great Iceni Queen. She who is unafraid to stand smeared in the blood of her enemies. She who withstood many horrors and witnessed countless injustices—and still found her power. Tattered and worn, beaten and bloodied she stands with us now.

Her voice cry's out, "Dig deep within yourselves my daughters. Find your voices, reclaim your power. You are part of a great line of brave sisters whose time has come to fruition. My story represents all of you. My gift to you all is that of unwavering strength of spirit, despite the cruelties and harshness of the world. Come together now, walk my path as one."

"Pick up your daggers, raise your bows and follow me into battle."

Why We Need the Boudica Spirit Today

Sharon Smith

Boudica (Latinized as Boadicea) was an Iceni woman born c. 30 CE, married at age 18 to Prasutagus, King of the Iceni, a tribe of early Britons. The memory of this ancient queen might never have survived the annals of Time, except for one important fact: She was a strong woman who was not content to sit back, after her husband died and left her a widow. Prasutagus had become a "client king" of Rome: The Roman general assigned to Britain, Suetonius Paulinus, pretty much let Prasutagus run things in his "neck of the woods" so long as he paid taxes to Rome and obeyed Paulinus and was loyal the Roman Emperor. But Boudica, on the other hand, did not favor Roman rule at all. And when the Romans sought to humiliate her, following Prasutagus's death, by beating her, raping her two young daughters, and taking her wealth and lands, she would not be silenced.

And here is where her Warrior Woman comes out in a blaze of glory. She rallied her tribe with brilliant, inspiring rhetoric and even got other Briton tribes that had been at odds with the Iceni to rally together with them under her banner to fight against the Romans. That, in itself, was quite an accomplishment. As a unified army, they marched on Camulodunum (Colchester), routing the Roman division there and sending the Imperial agent fleeing for his life to Gaul. Then Boudica and her troops stormed Londinium (London) and Verulamium (St. Albans), sacking and burning the towns.

Unfortunately, these Briton victories, under a WOMAN no less, angered Suetonius Paulinus, who struck back against the Britons with a vengeance and decimated Boudica's army. Boudica, herself, was not killed in the fray, but it is recorded that she took poison and ended her own life, rather than be taken as a slave of the Romans.

From that history, you may wonder why I see Boudica as a much-needed feminine icon for today: She lost, right? Well, she may have lost the battle, but she won the admiration of her people and even some of the Romans. One Roman historian, Cassius Dio, said of her, "The Britons mourned her deeply and gave her a costly burial."

Boudica remains a figure of sovereignty and strength for women everywhere. She could have sat back and allowed the Romans to take her lands and her possessions; she could have become a servant to Rome, as had her husband, Prasutagus. But Boudica had a backbone and it wasn't about to bend. She wanted her people to be free and their lands and possessions to belong to them, not to some foreign power. So, she fought back as valiantly and as fiercely as any male warrior.

What can we learn from this ancient Wild Warrior Woman?

- Conflicts come, and it's better to face them, rather than run from them.
- Stand your ground; set your boundaries and don't let others violate them.
- You're capable of much more than you think you are. So, think confidently; speak confidently; and act confidently.
- If hardships and difficulties come, rather than allowing them to defeat you, let them be the very stepping stones that will bring you closer to your goal.
- There's a time and a place to let that wild warrior woman out: Stay in touch with her! She'll let you know!
- Your freedoms are worth fighting for, even if, in the end, you lose the battle. Your willingness to stand up for those freedoms just may inspire others to do the same!

Boudica is one of my historical Sheroes. Whenever I hear her name, I feel a surge of pride in my womanity, because Boudica was a woman, just like you or me. What set her apart is that she walked in her sovereignty against all odds and, even in defeat, she ultimately won. Because she held on to the respect of her people, her nation and even her adversaries.

Now THAT's a Warrior Woman I'm proud to follow!

Warrior Queen
Barbara O' Meara

The Daughters of Boudicca

H. Byron Ballard

"Let us show them that they are hares and foxes
trying to rule over dogs and wolves."
-Boudicca's speech to her assembled troops, 60 CE.

One Roman historian described Boudicaa of the Eceni as being six feet tall, with flaming red hair to her hips. Standing before her statue near the Thames in London, I get a feel for the unquenchable spirit of the warrior-queen. As a feminist and a mother, I have great empathy for her story. Her husband ruled the Eceni in Britain in the early decades of the Common Era, when the Roman Empire was strengthening its hold in Western Europe. The Eceni was a client-kingdom of the Empire and upon the king's death, the Roman governor moved in to disarm the tribe and claim the ancestral lands. He didn't reckon with a woman who had been raised since childhood to rule her tribe, with or without her husband. He didn't reckon with Boudicaa.

Bailígí timpeall orm anois agus go neosfaidh mé scéal daoibh.
Is fada dhom ag cuimhneamh ar é a insint daoibh ach níor
fhéadas é go dtí so.*
Now I'll tell you a story—come gather around! I've long wanted to
tell you this but haven't been able to til now.

I am sitting in an auditorium with a large group of well-meaning and mostly white people who smell nice and have warm coats. We are singing about and talking about and dancing about peace. I do this a lot. These groups of gentle people wish desperately that the world were a better place and have a vague notion of peace as the answer to all the world's ills. Some think you can't have peace without justice, some quote King and Gandhi, and some believe that "we" are the ones we've been waiting for. I will see this group of people again in January, when we all participate in the annual

20

Martin Luther King Peace March downtown, which will culminate in prayers to gods I don't honor and boring speeches that are difficult to hear outdoors.

The dragon's teeth we've sown in the land between the beautiful Tigris and the mighty Euphrates continue to bear dark fruits, and my email inbox sees a new invitation at least weekly to protest in the town square. An overdue drink with a friend can only be scheduled after she's finished standing silently in black, round, and silent as an old Greek widow. "Peace," we mutter. "Peace at all costs. War is waste, madness, and folly. Bad, dark, dangerous."

But if war is bad, why do we love it so? We spend our treasure of children and gold on uniforms and weaponry, and we walk in fear of the enemy, the shadow, the other. We create the jihadist as a golem and cannot see his face or know his heart. The screens of our entertainment are filled with beautiful men and powerful women, armies of one, all they can be, held in reserve for regional emergency and national folly.

> Nach bhfeiceann tú os do chomhair é?
> Can't you see it there—in front of you?

A friend wished me joy and peace for the New Year. I replied that I'd take the joy but am unsure what is meant by "peace." Is it only the absence of war or is it the place where we can grow our crops and raise our young without fear? I live a peaceful life, barring the occasional return of my harsh temper. But I yearn towards the honor and glory of the warrior model that is so clearly expressed in our Western culture. Blood, gore, flashing steel, flame-tipped arrows. Armored horses, armored warriors. How can we make peace more glorious and honor-filled than war?

Some people think that in our long-ago past there were cultures of people who lived in rich areas that supplied all their Maslovian needs. These ancestors created art and left artifacts and I like to think they spent their time drinking wine and making love and growing perfect vegetables. Did they get bored with plenty? Did they grow tired of all those whole men hanging around with nothing to do but create art, whether in stucco or in the bedroom? Did they yearn for battle scars and jolts of adrenaline? Did they pine for a fight worth fighting and someone to declare their enemy?

The enemies came finally, spreading across the fertile plains from the windy steppes, burying their glorious dead in high-piled kurgans, filled with gold and slaughtered horses.

An cumin leatsa é?
Do you remember it?

I return to my ancestral lands, to the town that I called home for a brief and giddy time. I stand beside the slow-flowing old Thames with Big Ben at my back and the reconstructed Globe Theatre on my right. I stand before the majesty of a warrior-queen and seem to remember a time when women were wilder than we are now, more disciplined, more terrifying. When women held the reins of a war-chariot with the grip that now steers a stroller or a buggy full of food we haven't grown.

After a night of heavy beer and heavier food, my hair smells of smoke and my dreams are filled with flight. I take three steps, each one higher than the one before, and suddenly my body is aloft, floating for a time until I remember how to fly. I bend at the waist and my arms do the breaststroke, my legs undulating behind me. I go higher, past the electric lines and the t-shapes of power poles. Careful! I see the plains below me, and a river, and I follow the course of the water, deep into the countryside. There are mounds here, too, and standing stones waiting for the midwinter sun. Gunpowder dragons fire the night and I wake in the morning with aching shoulders, as though my flight was a shaman's work and not a dream at all.

An ghaoth aniar, bíonn sí fial.
The west wind is generous.

And so, I return to the Thames and the statue of Boudicca, queen
and war chief of the dead Eceni. For an Iron Age queen, she looks
peculiarly Victorian, almost pre-Raphaelite – the period when
Victoria's Albert commissioned this statue. She is graceful in her
strength, like a good dancer gone to seed. The daughters whose
names I never knew or can't remember crouch at her feet,
unwilling participants in their mother's war for their sakes. The
smell from the funky old river drifts past me, with some dust and
loose pages of the *Times*. I read the inscription on the stone
platform that holds the chariot and its occupants: "Regions Caesar
never knew/Thy posterity shall sway." At the base of the statue,
amongst the pigeon droppings, people have left offerings: some
wilted flowers, a few coins, and a silver ring.

Is cumin liom.
I remember.

Her name has changed since I was a girl when we called her
Boadicea. "The person who was thought worthy to be their leader
and who directed the conduct of the entire war, was Boudicca, a
Briton woman of the royal family and possessed of greater
intelligence than often belongs to women. This woman assembled
her army, to the number of some 120,000, and then ascended a
tribunal, which had been constructed of earth in the Roman
fashion. In stature she was very tall, in appearance most terrifying,
in the glance of her eye most fierce, and her voice was harsh; a
great mass of the tawniest hair fell to her hips; around her neck
was a large golden necklace; and she wore a tunic of divers
colours over which a thick mantle was fastened with a brooch.
This was her invariable attire. She now grasped a spear to aid her
in terrifying all beholders and spoke." -Cassius Dio. *History of
Rome*, Book LXII, Chapters 1-12.

That's how she is in this statue, and when I lived near Victoria Station, I often walked the length of Victoria Road, past Westminster's cathedral and abbey, and marveled at the lack of practicality. Why were there no reins on the horses? Why did she have no armor – not even leather slabs with fiddly bits of embedded metal? I had seen the metal work of her tribe in the British Museum and knew how adept they were with hammer and tongs. Was she wrapped in the ferocity of her rage, impervious to the spears of the piddling Romans? Her dress and those of her crouching daughters reveal every curve as if the chariot had risen from the depths of the river. The folds of bronze emphasize the woman-ness of the warrior, her perky breasts and massive thighs. I own those thighs, too, another legacy of home. Through a line of pigeons, I squint to see her face, to find a drop of personality, a stir of memory. But her face is impassive, aloof. She cannot smell the blood or the sweetish death smell. She does not hear the Morrigan and her ravens as they circle the fields of filth, of mud and piss and scraped flesh. Look at her, arms raised like a priestess, holding a spear, her pelvis arched forward.

Is beannaithe thú idir mhná.
Blessed art thou amongst women.

She had fallen into obscurity and is not mentioned by Bede the Venerable or Geoffrey of Monmouth or any of the mediaevalists. She is not part of the Arthur legend cycle, which embraces so much of the folk history of Britain, churning farm lore into glory. When she was rediscovered in the Renaissance through the translated writings of Tacitus and Cassius Dio (who lived and wrote long after she fell), she became the subject of plays and poems, and there is a mention of her in Holinshed's *Chronicles*. During the reign of Queen Victoria, this woman who had given her life to free her people from the tyranny of expanding empire, became the poster child for a new Rome. Victoria was called her namesake because the name "Boudicca" means victory (proto-Celtic *boudīko "victorious"; cf. Irish bua, Buaidheach: *Wikipedia.org*).

24

After the massacre of the Druids at Ynys Mona at the end of the world in Wales, where rebellion and stubbornness were answered with genocide, the Romans should have watched their backs. Maybe they were too far away from the heat of home. Perhaps they felt they were superior to the matted wool and blue faces of the tribal people. But they made a series of mistakes as we all do. Mistakes of pride and circumstance, when we stand on what is right, instead of thinking about what is best.

We understand from the Roman writers that upon the death of Boudicca's husband Prasutagus, the Emperor Nero and the King's daughters jointly inherited the tribal kingdom. The running of the tribe – the chiefdom – was left to Boudicca until the oldest daughter was of age, we suppose, though the Roman writers are not clear on this point. Nero, as we know, did not play well with others, and the Roman governor of Britain annexed the Eceni homelands and treasure. Boudicca assumed the barbarians from the East didn't understand tribal law and went with her daughters to speak with the man in charge. Maybe he didn't like uppity women; maybe the Druids on Mona had cursed him with impotence; maybe he had a toothache, we don't know. But he ordered the queen flogged and her daughters publicly raped. He would have been smarter to kill them all and place their heads on pikes. But he thought they were only women, and he knew how to deal with women. Humiliation and fear are always enough to shut us down. Our sense of self is always measured through the lens of other eyes, other hearts.

> Níor cheart é a denim.
> It shouldn't be like that.

She went home, like a good woman, and turned her daughters over to the tribal wise women who tended their wounds and made sure the daughters of a chieftain would never bear a soldier's brat. Maybe these old women bathed the queen's back in native tinctures and rubbed her with an ointment made from the fat of geese and the flowers that grew by the river. Since she was chief, there were servants to prepare her garments, arrange her transportation, bring her food and drink as she sat in the council circle. Did she send an envoy to the neighboring Trinivantes or were they her matrilineal tribe, spoiling for a fight with the overlords? Whatever the domestic details, this mother and woman and lover and widow raised an army of limed and blue-smeared warriors, freedom fighters, terrorists.

They moved first on a retirement community of former Roman soldiers at Camulodunum, a fortified place sacred to Camulos, a Celtic war god and home to the pork-barrel project that was the temple to Claudius. The museum of the modern city of Colchester squats on the same site. The massed warriors slaughtered the inhabitants and razed the city. The few old soldiers who holed up in the Claudian monstrosity were pulled out and hacked to death on the perfect Roman pavement. Then Boudicca turned to London.

> Tá sí ag teach.
> She is coming.

Suetonius Paulinus had returned from Ynys Mona, along a straight Roman road called Watling Street. He was hoping for reinforcements that had not come and so he deemed it prudent to leave London unprotected. He could not take the chance that she would destroy his legions, leaving the colonists in eastern Britain to the tender mercies of the Eceni queen. The Roman writers marveled that she led an army, and they attributed to Boudicca more intelligence than the average woman. No Roman woman would have done such a thing, presumably. The Celts didn't fight in tight battle formation as the Romans did, organized and deadly, but in a loosely structured gang, a horde that moved as a single ferocious entity. And that was enough to destroy the Ninth Legion Hispana, the one legion that did come between Boudicca and London.

How tired she must have been by then, the adrenaline high draining away. Did the future queen and her sister travel with their mother, learning the arts of war and rubbing salve on their offended parts? We don't know. Some scholars don't believe there ever was a Boudicca, though the archaeological record shows us places where towns were burned, and the carbon dating matches her dates. So, daughters of a mythical mother can't have much historical ground upon which to stand, can they?

She sacked and burned the young London and then turned her chariot toward Verulamium, where she again sacked, burned, and massacred. She was defeated in the end, of course, else she never would have been forgotten for so long. Boudicca escaped the final battle and legend has it she took poison rather than face being dragged through the streets of Rome in chains. We don't know what happened to her daughters. We don't even know where the warrior-queen is buried. Old rumor has it that she was interred with the spoils of her doomed war under King's Cross Station in London, but archaeologists say no. Fortune hunters reckon she's buried with all the plunder from three cities, but they haven't found her either. There are statues to her in some interesting places but no hard evidence, none at all.

Tá a fhios agam nach bhfuil sí ansin.
I know she is not there.

She didn't even save her people – they were used as an example to the poorer and smaller tribes in eastern Britain and were made slaves of the empire. They were also faced with starvation, because they had spent all their time and energy in fighting and not in farming. The Eceni had been one of the largest, richest tribes on the island but with the failure of the rebellion it faded into obscurity along with its war chief. Thousands dead on both sides, but the organized might of the Roman Empire prevailed for a time, though the Empire would soon find itself beset by wild tribes from the North and inner turmoil in Rome. The legions withdrew from Britain, from Gaul, from Africa, withdrew to protect Rome from the barbarians both within and without.

Tuigim anois.
I understand now.

I close my eyes as the river rushes past and I am there again, the wool of my tunic scratchy at my neck, my bare arms encircled with rings of gold. The wealth of any tribe is measured in land and livestock, in enough to share and enough to trade to someone else. Sometimes the acquisition of that wealth requires a tribe to move into more fertile lands, migrating to find the rich soil, the racing waters, the kind climate. If that land already has a tribe, then there is often a fight to the cultural death and the usurpers either destroy or are destroyed. We see that pattern in history again and again, less war than territorial imperative, driven by biological urges that are encoded into politics and religion.

Women have little to do with the march of history as we are taught it in our schools – women are the ones who wait at home or take on "men's work" in order to get by and keep the war machine going. Women are, and always have been, the ones who nurse the wounded and bury the dead. Women are rarely the ones who make the decision to go to war and the sacrifice of women and of the culture is the psychic and physical health of the next generation. But those who perish for the cause attain a kind of immortality not often granted ordinary mortals. Mortality makes the loss of the beloved not only bearable but also glorious.

Women and power. Women and death. Western culture gives us the glory of death and courage wrapped in a warrior package and occasionally a woman is the warrior. But how do we now – as the world twists and changes – fully step into our role as creator and destroyer? Have we the skills and the hearts to survive the unmaking of the old orders, keep our balance and walk the tightrope between aggression and strength, between power and glory and wiping a baby's nose?

We learn so much through the practice of living and through flying in our dreams. It is up to us now, as women, to define how the glory goes and when and to whom. Our quest as women is to find and claim our own kind of power in a world that has long denied us this privilege. How do we create a new world? As we midwife the death of the dominator system called patriarchy, we must organize and respond as women, consciously creating the world in our image. But first we must clarify that image and find the wit and courage to step into our own authentic power. We can look to the old systems for information, for inspiration as we gaze into the future of the planet and our species on it. We can honor the memory of the warrior-priestess, the queen, and the freedom fighter. Because it has fallen on us to birth the new world. Again.

We begin by acknowledging that those centuries of living under an autocratic and misogynistic culture has left gaping wounds in the human psyche. We accept that we must be healers as well as leaders, that we must salve spirits that are hurting and feed those that are hungry. We, as women, will define what a warrior is in this brave new world; then we will become that thing; we will model that for our sons and our daughters, for our grandchildren and our grandparents. For Boudicca and for her daughters, for we are all her daughters.

Fúmsa atá sé. Is cumin liom.
It's up to me. I remember.

Although the Irish I've used throughout is modern and Boudicca's tribe would have spoken a variety of Brythonic Gaeilge, I wanted readers to have a feel for the language.

The Midwives

Lucy Pierce

Take Back Your Power

Rebekah Myers

Sister, don't wait

Take back your power

Don't believe the priest and the pastor –
men limited by patriarchal perception
She is everywhere
She is everything
You do not need
the ladder built by men
to reach Her
Nothing stands between you
and your access to Goddess

Sister, don't believe
that you cannot make it on your own.

Take back your power

The way through may not be easy,
but you have a Circle of Sisters
upholding you,
ready to walk with you;
to help you find the way
Nothing stands between you
And your access to women's wisdom

Sister, you can heal

Take back your power

When the fist struck you
When the words cut you
When lies were spoken
When vows were broken
When support was absent
When there was no consent
When touch was unwanted
You can remain undaunted
Nothing stands between you
and your ability to rise

Sister, believe that you are enough

Take back your power

You don't need his permission
You don't need his blessing
Step away, step up, step out
Create, weave, gather, become
Be all that you are meant to be
He can't hurt you anymore
He can't burn you
He can't excommunicate you
He can't rob you
He can't molest you
He can't exclude you
He can't prohibit you
Nothing stands between you
and your own intelligence and capability

Sister, say to him,
"You Have No Power Over Me"

Take back your power

We are here
We will not leave you
She is here
She will not leave you

Be unafraid
Take back your power

Copyright © by Rebekah Myers, April 19, 2021

We Rise

Melody Bergman

Rage burned in the air and lifted the hairs on my arms, burrowing itself beneath my skin. Rage – not mine, not yet. It lingered dormant in my blood, lifetimes upon lifetimes leading me to where I was, mothers after mothers after mothers. I carried them with me. Quivering on the floor, shards of a broken mirror lie scattered around me like fractals, sharp totems of memories of myself smiling at my own reflection. I remember using that mirror to dye my hair on an autumn night before the start of school, nimble gloved fingers massaging my transformation into my long locks. I was just a child. Made to feel small, to be silent and sit in the corner with my hands in my lap and lips pursed. I was told my words didn't matter; I was nothing more than a bambi-legged animal still learning to walk in this world.

My arms ached, bruises blooming where hands had squeezed and hauled me up before throwing me into the tall mirror pinned to the bathroom door. In that moment I wished I'd just passed through it.

The reflection wasn't necessary in order to see myself eye-to-eye, to recognize the strength that had always been inside me, known in my marrow. I didn't need a mirror's gaze to know my teeth were gritted, jaw ticking in subtle ripples beneath my skin. There it was – the spark of rebirth, the call of mothers still living in my blood and ushering me forth. They danced to the drum beneath my ribs, the primordial beat from which all things rise. I wasn't alone, I'd never be alone. I held an entire army in my veins, ready to draw up arms and fight with me.

Those hands expected me to remain broken and weeping on the floor amid the sparkling, crooked sea. The mirror and memories around me shattered, but I didn't. There would be no crumbling in defeat, no superstitions of misfortune. I rose to my feet, broke through the top layer of earth and grew, reaching for the sun. I would not let this kill me. I would not sit quiet and pretty. The lioness in me stood up that day and roared, hair long and wild like war banners fluttering in the wind. She spat resistance in the face of those who told her she didn't matter. It wasn't true, it never was.

From that day forth I continued growing, whispering to the seeds in my veins and sowing them in blood. They inhaled and exhaled cycles like seasons, carrying me through bone-cold winters and sweltering summers. Setbacks were only part of the process. No matter how far I fell, I'd always find a way to ascend. It was a battle I promised myself I'd never lose. To this day I still march forward, countless kindred at my side and in my heart. We all continue onward, walking forth in resilience. Together we rise.

Warrior
Lucy Pierce

Warpaint – Mourning under Boudicca

Joey Morris

Today I am in mourning with a full face of make-up.

This is perhaps not the way I envisaged a stage of mourning, but it brought the wistful smile of remembrance to my lips as I painted them and added a little shimmer.

I recently lost my Nana, and both She and my Grandmother had a very survivor vibration to their personalities in different ways. My Nana was an Ice Queen, she had perfected the eyebrow arch of disdain and when confronted had what I refer to as "posh bitch" mode; I would hear her confront sales people on the telephone and would smirk to myself - if they had messed something up and dared tell her that she was in the wrong, they were about to get a very articulated telling off.

My Nana saw ghosts, and was always intrigued (quietly) about life after death.

My Grandmother was cheekier; rounder, softer in general with a gleam of naughtiness in her eye. Her signature move when she was annoyed at my Grandfather was to blow a raspberry and give the middle finger behind his back in one hilarious movement. She believed in a small shot of whiskey and lemonade every day to "chase the cobwebs away" and had a variety of clues to her inner witchiness, such as the dried herbs in the kitchen window that nobody touched, or the fact the garden looked prize-winning under her folklore educated fingertips.

Something they both had in common though, was the "keep calm and carry on" mentality of those who had survived wartime.

At some stage, they both referred to makeup as warpaint and I certainly picked up this habit early, being the only teenager I knew who referred to cosmetics as such.

I loved the idea it could be a weapon against the world; armouring me against a crappy day, or if I had to see people I disliked, or just giving me a little more energy as I added a little shimmer.

I have definitely carried both my grandmothers into my energy, especially with my Witchcraft, both seeing the spirits of the dead from a very early age and feeling a close kinship to nature spirits. I embody both women's confrontational tactics; getting VERY haughty if I am angered, and simultaneously playing with my cheeky inner fox, only rising to arguments if I really feel the need to. My inner warrior has certainly been shaped by their generation, failing as my parents did to provide any kind of traits that were worthy of being a role-model (simply providing the what-not-to-do's and what-not-to-be's instead).

There was and is something both warrior and witch about my grandmothers.

They lived in a very different time, my Grandmother regaled me with tales of ballroom dances in the village hall, and my Nana was a secretary for a very well thought of firm when doing so was difficult for women.

Neither spoke much about the war, a snippet here and there, talk about blackout curtains, my Grandma working on making bombs at boots pharmacy when prior she had merely been a dinner-lady at the local school, the wake of destruction following bombings. But generally, their attitude was more on life as it was; the enjoyment of life, both being lucky to have not lost their husband, and entertaining their grandchildren every week for years.

My favourite war time story about my Grandma was one I only found out about after her death.

It turned out in war time she had been making alcohol in her bathtub and selling it on the black market. The idea of her sneakily being a bootlegger makes me grin internally.

Both these women flouted the rules in their own way.

My Nana came from a very Christian household who didn't approve particularly of the man she fell in love with, my Grandpop, who she married anyway. She also smoked like a chimney, ate whatever she wanted, drank on occasion, and reveled in her freedom. To many she seemed stiff and proper and stern, but I don't think they took the full measure of her upbringing into account. Moving away from Wales was pure rebellion, to my knowledge, none of her peers would have dared.

She also had a dry witty sense of humour that I adored growing up.

The spirit of rebellion flowed within them, and it planted that seed in me.

How could I be anything else?

So, I paint my face with warpaint and feel their loss today.

Shadow Work

Kathy Barenskie

I dreamt a song of dying,
a death that's a life untold.

Eyes closed,
Breath deepening,
I Step in ...
Dark silent waters.
Deep well.
Pulsating with the promise of a life fulfilled.
Walls crumbling, uncovering a mirror to the mystery of my Soul.
Taking another breath, I Dive deeper.
Sinking further,
Down, down into cold murky waters.
Past crumbling walls.
Down into futures, past, present.
Keep breathing.
Down past the confines of my mind,
leaving this world behind.
Entering into the silent place that directs my waking hours.
Entering the dream, I claim my life.
To become the dream,
not the dreamer.

Who knew there was such a treasure,
Buried Deep inside of me?
Pure as liquid gold,
As sweet as the honey bee.
A pool of infinite shadow.
Collected from long past morrows.
Deep pool of guarded feelings,
a Well of infinite sorrows.

Each salty tear a diamond,
a jewel forged from black coal.
The heat from my heart a furnace,
that blocked from the start, my soul.
Yet now I cry those tears
Hot, messy, liquid gold
Now I dive in the pool of my shadow,
swim deep in the well of my soul.

Releasing the dragon that guarded,
treasure buried deep within.
Releasing raw, hot feelings,
let the awakened dream begin.
I dreamt a song of dying,
a death that's a life untold.
Now I dream a dance of
living, a life that's free and bold.
Deep pool of infinite sorrows,
Is a blessing not a sin.

Awoke to a dance of living,
A life that's free and bold.

The Importance of SHEroes

Trista Hendren

It is difficult for me to imagine how different my life would have been had I been taught *any* sort of HERstory growing up. It was not until I started Women's Studies in 1994 that I began to see all that had been hidden from me—and finally got a glimpse of all the power I had yet to reclaim.

As a Christian teenager, the legend of Boudicca would have given me an entirely opposite view of what was possible for women than what I had been led to believe through reading the Bible and attending church.

Mona Eltahawy captured my approach to raising my daughter in *Headscarves and Hymens*.

> "What if instead of breaking their wildness like a rancher tames a bronco, we taught girls the importance and power of being dangerous?
>
> I want to bottle-feed rage to every baby girl so that it fortifies her bones and muscles. I want her to flex, and feel the power growing inside her as she herself grows from a child into a young woman."[5]

In addition to physical strength and emotional intelligence, our daughters also must learn HERstory.

I realized early on that my daughter was not going to learn much about this at school (despite my requests!), so I took it upon myself to seek out books and learning opportunities to teach her.

---

5 Eltahawy, Mona. *Headscarves and Hymens: Why the Middle East Needs a Sexual Revolution*. HarperCollins Publishers, 2015.

Some of my favorite memories with Helani were reading the entire female section of the *Who Was* series[6] for children. She brought some of her favorites with her to Norway, even though we only had 4 suitcases between us when we moved here.

Unfortunately, they do not offer a book on Boudicca—which is not surprising. Even the limited HERstory children are taught is usually the same handful of (mostly relatively tame) women. In her biography of Boudicca, Vanessa Collingridge wrote:

> "There are not many female heroes in our history books and even fewer were known for having the same untamed thatch of red hair that cursed my childhood. I was too much of a tomboy to be drawn to stories of damsels in distress or cloistered princesses yet here was a queen who fought for her people on muddy and bloody battlefields; a perfect role-model for an ungainly ginger child. Boudica – or Boadicea as she was to us then – became my personal mascot, someone who I could look up to with a quiet sense of communion. The girls could have their blonde-haired Barbies; I would have my kick-ass carrot-top Queen."[7]

I believe all girls should grow up knowing about this kick ass Queen. For those of us who did not, this anthology will serve as a starting point. Joey Morris has also written a children's book about her that we will publish shortly.[8]

Mainstreaming women's history is long-overdue. Gerda Lerner wrote, "Women's history is the primary tool for women's

---

6   When we worked through these around 2012-2013, there were significantly more men than women represented. I wrote to the publisher about this at the time and never received a response. As of 9/1/21, by my count, fewer than one-quarter of the books are about women (47 of the 204 titles). https://www.penguinrandomhouse.com/series/DWY/who-was
7   Collingridge, Vanessa. *Boudica: A Groundbreaking Biography of the True Warrior Queen*, Ebury, 2006.
8   Morris, Joey. *My Name is Boudica*. Girl God Books, 2022.

emancipation."[9] When women learn their rich HERstory, there is a significant shift that ripples through their entire way of be-ing.

Every woman I know who took Women's Studies in college talks about how their whole world sort of opened up with their first class. Why do we deprive our girls of this experience throughout most of their education? Is it possible more children would love going to school if it related back to them directly?

How can they have heroes that don't reflect who they are?

Our heroes are important: They guide us to where we can go (if we dare) and save us from our own limiting beliefs about ourselves. *How do we guide our children to find role models who will empower them?*

The importance of giving our daughters and granddaughters a woman-affirming education cannot be overstated. I have a lot of grief centered around having to spend most of my life working to re-program and heal myself. It has been a devotion of mine for far too long. I wanted to give my daughter a different foundation—and I have, to the extent I can. That said, even in so-called 'progressive' Norway, my daughter has only had one-day of women's history.

Yesterday, my daughter lamented that she could never share anything I taught her at school if she wanted to get good grades. She said that the teachers only wanted her to parrot back what they taught—which of course, is all male-centric.

How can it be, that in 2021, my daughter has no chance academically to learn the exact things that have been foundational in my healing? Why are we still depriving girls and young women of this wisdom?

---

9   Lerner, Gerda. *The Creation of Patriarchy.* Oxford University Press; Reprint edition, 1987.

Children need to learn about people that they can identify with for guidance and strength. Abby Wambach wrote that, "Women have had to find themselves within content presented from the male perspective forever. It's essential to flip this and allow men the opportunity to find themselves within content presented from a woman's perspective."[10]

If you have boys in your life, they need to learn from this perspective as well.

Given the fact that most of us are not taught anything other than white male history in school, it is important that we take up the task of educating ourselves—and our daughters, sons, and grandchildren. As Assata Shakur wrote, "No one is going to give you the education you need to overthrow them. Nobody is going to teach you your true history, teach you your true heroes, if they know that that knowledge will help set you free."[11]

Girls and boys must begin to learn HERstory.

It is time to teach our children about Boudicca!

---

10 Wambach, Abby. *Wolfpack: How to Come Together, Unleash Our Power, and Change the Game*. Celadon Books, 2019.
11 Shakur, Assata. *Assata: An Autobiography*. Lawrence Hill Books; 1st edition, 2001.

The Empowered Child

Jeanne Raines

Boudicca's Dream

Kaalii Cargill

The last sunset of the millennium glowed on the horizon, a blushing promise of the New Age. The Queen stood alone on the balcony outside her rooms, watching the light fade. It was here she had come for all the endings and beginnings since the first year of her marriage to the King. They had been granted more time even than had been promised them in those far off, glorious days. Time enough to build a world of peace and justice, to fulfill the prophecies and defy the fate predicted by the soothsayers. Nevertheless, it had been a near thing.

Gwen shuddered to think what might have been, her long dark curls rippling down her back like the snakes her sister-in-law had once kept in her tower. It had been a long time since Gwen had thought of Morgana. Perhaps it was the turning of the Age that had stirred the old memories.

Gwen gave thanks to the powers that be for all that had come to pass. The land was fruitful, the people content. Not for them the Dark Ages and troubles that had beset the rest of Europe. Not for them the endless striving for conquest and the grief of war. She sighed, breathing in the freshness of winter.

They had celebrated the Winter Solstice just ten days earlier, with a bonfire big enough to light the night sky and the sacred words of the Druids to name the turning of the season. Gwen sometimes wondered what would have become of the world if the Old Ways had been lost\ and the religion of the Father God had taken hold. She shivered again, pulling her cloak close around her.

Footsteps in the room behind made her turn. She had trusted he would come to watch the sunset with her, but she allowed herself a sigh of relief that he was in time. He came to stand with her, taking her hand.

"It makes me think of what might have been," he murmured, looking out into the distance.

Gwen nodded. "I know."

Someone else entered the room behind them. Gwen smiled. She had known he would come, also.

Lance came to stand with them as the world turned and the last light of the twentieth century disappeared. "I have been thinking of the beginning today," he said quietly.

The three of them moved inside. Gwen sat between the two men, on the long couch facing the fire.

"I wonder what Merlin would say about what we've done with the time he gave us." Gwen looked into the flames, as if she might see the old Druid looking back at her.

"He'd snort and harrumph, and ask if there was anything to drink," said Lance, smiling at the thought.

"He'd ask what we had planned for the new century and complain about the oak groves we've lost." The King looked genuinely worried at the prospect of a lecture from his old teacher.

"Not so," said Gwen emphatically. "There are more groves here than anywhere in the world, and they are still used by the people. And it's the only place where the old religion survived."

The men nodded, remembering when the first Christians had come with their stories of a Father God and their disregard for the Gods and Goddesses of old. They had wanted to burn the oak groves or fell the great trees to build halls for their God. The King had offered them a place amongst his people, but forbade the felling of the ancient trees, and the preaching of their religion. They had left soon after.

Artur had done that with all who came, offering them a place in the land he had unified. Some stayed, their blood and customs blending with the old blood of the land, strengthening it. The wars of the world had not bothered them, protected as they were by the old magic. A traveller had once told them that the protection cast over Albion and the islands was like a grey cloak in winter twilight. For centuries there had been stories told of how the land seemed to fade from sight if approached from outside with any intention for harm. Gwen smiled, sending a silent blessing to Merlin, wherever he was.

#

Three months later the first green shoots heralded the new season, and the three of them rode north along one of the roads running the length and breadth of the land along the ley lines. Gwen hummed a tune she remembered from her childhood, a simple melody celebrating the return of the sun.

With no warning at all, an old man stepped out from behind one of the huge rocks lining the road. "Hail, travellers. Well met!" he called in a voice that echoed along the road like a fey wind.

Artur yelled and lunged off his horse to grab the old man. Who held the King as if he was a boy and danced with him on the road. They all sat together under the trees, the dappled light of spring flickering over their faces as they spoke of the past and then of the future.

"You promised us time enough to realise the dream," said Gwen, sitting close to the old Druid.

Merlin nodded, his white beard bobbing up and down.

"It took longer than we expected," said Artur, smiling ruefully.

"Building something always takes longer than tearing it down, my son. The rest of the world has done quite a bit of both since I hid Albion in the mists."

A frisson of unease made Gwen ask, "Why are you here now?"

"Ah. Not lost any of your brightness over the years, have you?" Merlin fixed Gwen with his hawk like eyes.

Artur and Lance frowned, wondering what had called forth her question.

"I come with a choice for you," said Merlin, looking at each of them in turn. "The world had changed. There are many wonders out there beyond the mists. I was thinking that you might like to be a part of it."

The three people Merlin loved most in all the worlds stared back at him, mouths hanging open.

He laughed. "No need to look so shocked. It is a New Age after all."

They talked then of what the world might hold for Albion. Merlin told them of the wonders of electricity, cars, trains, and planes. He spoke of computers and the extraordinary development of the World Wide Web. They listened like children entranced by tales of mythical worlds.

"But what of the people?" asked Gwen. "Are they happy? Is there peace? Does everyone have a home and food to eat?"

Merlin shook his head sadly and told them of the wars, the famines, and the epidemics. He spoke of horrors not seen in Albion for over a thousand years, horrors they could not even imagine. As the shadows of evening reached them, Merlin rose to leave.

"Look for me on the summer solstice. Tell me then what you have decided."

Three months later, Gwen, Artur, and Lance sat together on the balcony outside Gwen's rooms, watching the sun set in the west. Soon they would join the others in the oak grove for the ritual, but there was something to be said first.

"I cannot sacrifice what we have built for the things Merlin described, no matter how wondrous they may be." Gwen's face was filled with regret and a fierce determination. She had no way of knowing it, but she looked in that moment like her ancient kinswoman, Boudicca, the Iceni Queen who had rallied the tribes against the Roman invasion and made possible the dream that had become Albion.

Artur nodded. "Nor I."

Lance smiled at his two dearest friends. "Of course not. What's it all been for otherwise?"

They rose to join the line of people processing to the grove. Merlin's laughter echoed on the summer breeze.

Queen Boudicca

Molly Roberts

Rebellion and Reverence

Victoria Wilson-Randall

I stand,
my feet clad in chunky boots,
planted in the echoes of your footsteps,
in reverence and rebellion.
Your righteous rage bled into the soil, and it rises,
through these soles,
into my soul,
travelling through my veins like lava,
igniting my inner flame,
and it rises
and rises
burning away the wool that has been clouding my vision and
softening the edges of reality.
I squint through the painful light,
salty bitter tears fall,
as I see
the dying earth,
the power corruption,
the rules,
the lies,
the devastation and destruction.
My head arches back toward the sky, as my lungs scream a battle
cry,
I breathe
and shake
and pray that those awake will hear it.
The words spit through gritted teeth
"They called us witches, but they cast the greatest spell
Illusion,
manufactured delusion,
but now
We rebel."

When The Colour Of Emotion Floods The Nervous System

Earth Mothers and daughters surviving invasion and the stereotypes of misogyny.

Claire Dorey

"I Am Woman Hear Me Roar." -Helen Reddy

Rape is red, blue and black.

Red is blood. Blue is bruises. Black is trauma.

Red is the menstrual Muladhara, a downward cleansing tide of energy that connects the 'blood root of existence' to Mother Earth. Mula 'root' and dhara 'in flow' are primordial, intelligent, purifying actions – completed by the moon. Muladhara flows down to Gaia and up to Divine Female Cosmic Power. To violate this sanctum is the ultimate act of savagery, upon the survivor, the Goddess and the creative force of life itself.

Blue is shock. It is the liminal, safe space above the body, where the soul escapes to, when the body-mind freezes, and pain can no longer be endured. Just as bruises fade, blue cedes to the violet of cosmic 'knowing'. Trauma unleashes a state of hyper awareness. Learning to surf this wave unlocks boundless vaults of intuition and clarity. A healed survivor can never be fooled.

Black is the abyss. Dissociation. Disconnect. Chaos. A coffin-shaped space of grief and mourning. Black is damage and flashbacks. The cosmic void. The place of death, internal battles, self-loathing, renewal, recovery, resolve and magic. The womb of time where the immense and terrifying forces of destruction and creation reside.

When a daughter is raped, her mother is reminded of her own rape. When Red becomes Rage it is Raw, as raw as the welts lacerating Boudicca's flesh, from her public whipping. Boudicca's story is about harnessing the molten menstrual larva of Red Rage as it heaves, in response to the attack upon her daughters, like vomit, out of every orifice.

When Catus Decianus seized Boudicca's land, he threw her daughters, Isolda and Siora, to the slaves and soldiers, as if he was throwing meat to a dog. This was a Roman rape, in the tradition of the spectacle of the Colosseum, where lions are slaughtered and gladiators fight for survival before a salacious crowd, frenzied with blood-lust. Violence for gratuitous violence sake. It was a trophy rape, of hierarchy, nationalism, and public humiliation, where slaves and soldiers, fight for their master's scraps.

It was a political rape, a culture clash, between the extreme patriarchy of the conquerors and the matrifocal values of the colonised. It was Rome telling Briton, her Warrior Women had no voice. No more decision making, owning land, or inheriting titles. It was the ultimate form of power and control, silencing ALL women.

In Rome there were good women and there were bad women – madonnas and whores. Good women were good mothers – defined by the values of the Roman male. Other behaviours were viewed as stepping out of line.

Isolda and Siora were no more than twelve when they were attacked and Boudicca was forced to watch.

What sort of sick regime brutalises the vulnerable like this? How do a mother and child recover from such sadism?

Fight is Red. Flight is Blue. Freeze is Black. The Fight, Flight, Freeze mechanism can kick in so violently, it cripples the survivor, possibly for years. Confusion. Anxiety. Numbness. Disconnect. Goodbye feeling safe. Hello bouts of shame, flashbacks and complex trauma. Victims and witnesses of violence need prompt physical and psychological care. There can be no rights or wrongs in recovery. It is a personal journey.

History doesn't mention healing, so I've woven this scenario:

Here I am, crouching behind a deadfall in a forest clearing, watching a chimeric creature crawl, weeping, and screaming, towards a grove of oak trees. "Mother Earth! Comfort me!" Screams the beast and I realise she is human.

Intuition tells me not to intervene, as this woman is broken, yet strong. I sense that if she sees me, she will kill me. Powers that I don't understand have been unleashed. If I am to survive, I need to stay silent.

I find a glittering coin in the undergrowth. On one side: a horse, with a crescent shaped Moon Crown and a Wheel of Life. On the reverse: concentric circles, a central trefoil and four directions, marked with dots – perhaps celestial references? It could be the aerial view, of these oaks, as seen from the cosmos, looking back at Earth, a Celtic temple.

Green is the colour of the heart, serenity, and healing but this is a forest emerging from winter so there is no green here. It is a forest in its brown stage, desolate, yet welcoming. Brown contains all the colours of the forest; greens, ochres, Earth pigments. Brown, in all its infinite variety, from limestone, to the achromatic dark of the peat bog, is the colour of Mother Earth. Brown is nature in decay, poised to regenerate.

Mother Nature is the ultimate force in forgiveness. You can cut Her down, burn Her and She will grow back and when She dies, She nourishes Herself. That is life force – the power of Animacy.

No wonder Pagans trusted Her with their healing. Are any religions comparable in power to Mother Nature?

The woman is dragging herself across the forest floor, to be close to the Tellus Mater, for strength and comfort. Her mane of hair is the shade of fox and as she rises, she lets out an enormous bile curdling bellow, a desolate cry of wounding and sadness. She wears a stitched rabbit skin cloak, and her tunic is in tatters, soaked with blood. Her nostrils prick as she picks up a scent – my scent maybe? I'm about to run when she throws off her clothes and stands there naked, primal. The thick gold cuff around her neck anchors her to humanity. Her ghostly white skin is lacerated with whip marks. I want to flee, but I don't, because if she catches me, I would be no match for her. Best to stay crouching behind the deadfall.

She moves towards the grove of matronly oaks, approaching from the West, face to the East, arms outstretched to the North and South, just as a funnel of eerie zodiacal light rises above the horizon.

As dawn seeps into the forest Boudicca calls out, "AAAA-NNNN-DDD-RRRR-AAAA-SSSSS-TEEEE."

Boudicca is silhouetted against the diffuse, crepuscular rays. She hangs between the tree trunks like a spider, shaking the branches, to wake the nature spirits. As she yells, throwing her rage into the universal void, her aura increases into a corolla of flames. The universe reciprocates with a flow of dynamic energy. The laws of abundance are activated.

"ANDRASTE." She yells, stamping her feet, sending vibrations, through the tree roots and mycorrhizal networks, out across the forest floor.

"AANNDDRRAASSTTEE."

"I call upon the Deadly Black North Wind to unleash your immense forces. Revenge will be mine!"

A swirling mist eclipses the light and when it clears, it reveals the silhouette of two girls, slumped at Boudicca's feet.

"Why did you do this to them?" She wails. "My beautiful daughters."

As Boudicca roars, two translucent figures step out of her body and stand beside her, shoulder to shoulder. Boudicca could be a priestess of the Goddess Andraste or SHE IS Andraste – the triple Goddess: Andraste, Andate and Boudicca.

"Step out of the shadows." orders Andraste, who is veiled in healing white.

She summons with arms outstretched and I move, as if by osmosis, into the inner sanctum, where Boudicca, Isolda and Siora lie, in coma, gone to their 'black place', on a soft carpet of moss.

The lunar Goddesses pour Allium ursinum, honey, wine, goat's milk, copper particles and bile into a bronze bowl and mix a poultice.

"A sort of AncientBiotic?" I ask.

"Well sort of!" They laugh. "But not so ancient to us of course!"

"This is Apotropaic Magic. Spiritual invocation and Mother Nature work with the antimicrobial compounds. Healing is a communal, divinatory and cosmological event."

We align their bodies, head in the East, feet in the West and apply the poultice. I can feel a joyous vibration – the act of healing is a reciprocal event. We embalm their bodies with comfrey leaves and wrap them in the rabbit skin cloak, like a pastry parcel.

"Now we let them sleep." Says Andate.

"Are we going to leave them here?" I ask.

"Yes, for the gestation period of nine days and nine nights."

"Why nine?" I ask.

"It's a sacred number." Replies Andraste.

"What do we do now?"

"We sit and wait."

For nine days the sun rises over the convalescing bodies. For nine nights the moon, Milky Way, and bats soar across the forest canopy – nature in cyclical, energetic motion.

In the moonlight we drum to the universe.

"These moon baths will change the vibration from trauma to healing." Whispers Andate.

It rains, the sun shines, we wake from turbulent dreams, covered in frost and on day six I notice the forest is full of horses.

"Boudicca's horses." Explains Andraste.

The waiting gives me the sacred space to confront my own relationship with Rage. I am conditioned not to express it. Subtly, silenced by society, I silence myself, before I am silenced. I have learnt to be small. Yelling is a rare event. Yelling with abandon never happens.

Watching Boudicca shaking the boughs, spewing out rage and hurling it at the universe, I realise I want to find the anger buried deep within myself.

"I wouldn't recognise anger if I found it." I say.

"Your anger is buried beneath layers of low frequency, resentment, shame, self-loathing and fear." Replies Andate.

"Face your fears and you will find anger."

"Should I jump in the river to purge myself and scream until I pass out?"

"Ha Ha! Noooo!" Shrieks Andate. "We are tough people, used to wading through peat bogs. You are soft, like the nancy boy Romans, who bathe in hot water. They perish in our rivers!"

"Awareness is key to healing." Explains Andraste.

A spider runs across my leg, and I flinch.

"You will never conquer fear until you can live alongside the spider." Andate lectures me.

"And understand the cosmic weavers and spinners of fate."

"Unpick the samskara of your neural pathways that run inwards, from STIMULUS to FEAR."

"Spin them, so they connect outwards, like the spider web, to the abundance of the universe."

"Will Boudicca and her daughters be healed?" I ask, as the nine-day healing nears its end.

"Healing should not be a solitary process. We have connected with the sovereign consciousness of the universe. However, we cannot process their trauma for them. Our healing is divinatory. It's about knowing the next step, with NO REGRETS."

"Who knows how they will respond when they wake up! They have free will!"

When Boudicca wakes, 'Fight' is the adrenaline response that continues to course through her nervous system. Isolda and Siora are stuck in Freeze.

A mother never, ever gets it right. Is this 'blame' a hang up from the Roman edict of 'good mothers and bad mothers' – a notion that eventually spirals out of control – into the ridiculous sentiment that women are 'the villains of humanity'? How did we ever accept this nonsense?

It must be hard for a mother not to see her children as an extension of herself. Their wounds are her wounds. Did traumatised Boudicca suffer narcissistic wounding? A person with a label is easier to understand, but should anyone be given a label? Labels confine. Crazy wisdom frees!

There is a sea change of energy, as the tribes unite and prepare for war. The Lunar Goddesses ditch their veils and strap their breast plates on. Boudicca rides her chariot, joining the ranks of the Chariot Driving Goddesses: Nike, Athena, Minerva, Cybele, Flidais, Eos, Ushas, Eoster, Bellona, Ausrine, Aurora, Selene and Luna. The wheel of fate is starting to turn.

In the Celtic Wheel of Time, East represents the Earth and possibilities. When Boudicca liberates a hare, Andraste's symbol, from beneath her robe, I'm guessing it runs to the auspicious East, to the rising sun – the direction of the Dawn Chariot Goddesses – a good omen!

Dawn is associated with yellows and reds. When Cassius Dio described Boudicca's colours as 'xanthotatos' was it an emotional response to the blazing bronze aura she exuded, fired by red rage, evoking images of Aurora, the saffron robed, chariot driving, Goddess of Dawn?

Fighting for the vulnerable, Boudicca evokes images of the lion flanked, Goddess Cybele and Sekhmet, the leonine, Egyptian Solar Goddess of War.

The Fierce, protective, proud, and wild Lioness, Boudicca confused the Romans – sons of war god Mars – who were used to stereotyping women. Did Dio, in awe, associate flaming, female Boudicca with fiery, male god Mars?

Boudicca's army decimated Camulodunum, Verulamium and finally Londinium. We join her, smashing into the last standing Villa, where a young woman, the last Roman survivor, shelters. Octavia is neat and fragrant, with hair piled high. As a married woman she wears the stola, to show her virtue. Her palla drapes to veil her face.

"You understand I must kill you?" Thunders Boudicca, sword in hand, tearing away the palla, revealing a child's innocent face staring back.

"I am sorry for what Catus Decianus did to your daughters." Mumbles petrified Octavia.

"I think they may be the same age as me."

This statement pierces Boudicca's desensitised heart.

"How old are you?" She asks.

"Twelve." Replies the child.

Will battle-hardened, scarred, and bloody Boudicca murder this child? Has she lost all humanity?

"Despite your fate, I was jealous of your freedom." appeases Octavia, as weary Boudicca slumps on the couch. She aches all over.

"To hear you roar like a lion has been an inspiration to me."

"I'm rarely allowed to speak. I have never raised my voice. When I go out, I veil my face and have a chaperone. I am married to a forty-year-old. Despite living in comfort, I am a slave to Rome."

"Look what they do to the daughters of Rome!" Wails Boudicca, putting down her sword.

"Did you ever wonder what it is like for your daughters?" Ventures Octavia.

"It must be hard for them to follow in your shadow."

"Did they ever have a voice?"

"Do you forgive yourself for what happened to them?"

The villa oozes with comfort, whilst outside it's carnage. Carcasses of women hang from pikes, their severed breasts, stitched into their mouths. Rome's moral code of 'pudicita' – public virtue and modesty – is vengefully ransacked.

"When you kill me will you turn me into a war trophy?" Asks Octavia.

"I pledged to show no mercy." Boudicca wails, battling her conscience.

"I have lost my softness... And my mind! Your death will be no victory. My victory will be to retrieve my humanity."

As the Red Rage softens, it subsides to PINK – a four petalled, lotus pink – Mother's Love.

"Come on." She says to Octavia. "Let's get you out of here."

Boudicca's story is a warning from history: DO NOT ABUSE THE VULNERABLE.

AD 60 – the year of Boudicca's death – the new world age was still dawning. Aries, the age of expanding Empire and warring sons of Mars, gave way to Pisces, when epic battles for women's rights were fought and lost. Eventually women gained some ground.

As Aquarius dawns it could be the Golden Age. Steering our Dawn Chariots, shining like the Solar Goddess, we can heal millennia of misogyny. As the Goddess steps out of the shadows, into Her Leonine Prowess, we will ROAR LIKE LIONS.

Let the sons of Mars go and live on the desolate planet they seem so keen to colonise. Meanwhile we will nurture Mother Earth.

Be Bold
Lady Wolf

Blind Spots (The Art of Survival)

Kathy Barenskie

We all have our blind spots.
One of Hers is telling herself She is 'normal'.
This despite the loneliness, anxiety, the hair, the clothes and big boots.
At least She believes it.
"What is normal?"
The child inside whispers:
"Don't forget that feeling when your tummy curled around a fist."
And, She is happy now.
I watched Her grow.
From a dark thing, hiding in a corner from the monsters,
into a 'light filled Goddess.'
She is Boudicca, warrior Queen
She liberates Sisters who hide behind boring lives.
Carpets, curtains, cars.
Rock star husbands with frumpy worn out wives.
"Fuck off with that kinda blind spot!
Rather Hers, than that big gapping mistake of unhappiness they call a married life."
She tells Herself this.
Though unconvinced.
Her child inside whispers:
"Don't forget that feeling when the monsters ripped your insides apart."
Yet, She is happy now.
I watched Her grow.
She can put up with so much pain now,
She is Boudicca,
Goddess of War!
Years rolling on now.
Into near life passing, or at least past middle age somewhere.

Still seeking growth, picking battles.
While the child inside remains hidden from the monsters,
who are long since gone.
Yet, She is happy now, even with her blind spots.
She is Boudicca, riding into battle on her chariot of dissent.
Denial is an existence too.

Dreaming of Boudicca

Barbara O' Meara

The Audacious Spirit

Maureen Owen

**"Courage calls to courage everywhere,
and its voice cannot be denied." -Millicent Fawcett**

For as long as I can remember I've heard Boudicca's call, across the far reaches of time and space. I feel her courageous spirit calling me. When I close my eyes, I can see her, and the army she has amassed to rebel against the brutality of Roman occupation. I see her long red hair, tattoos, and steely glare. I can feel the dignity she holds herself with, her refusal to be shamed and her fierce determination. It is as if I am Iceni, a descendant of this ancient tribe being called to be courageous, called back to my full power, called to unshackle my soul from the tyranny of patriarchal oppression.

This is the story of how Boudicca's audacious spirit has been a constant companion in my life and a voice that could not be denied.

I did not become defiant. I've always been that way.

My love of Boudicca and her audacious spirit began when I was a child. Back then her spirit called as intensely as it does today although I did not yet know her name and story. Nonetheless her spirit permeated my soul. My first memory, when three or four, is of observing the way women in my family were treated, thinking "this is not right, it's not meant to be like this". So, I cannot say I became defiant, as it seems I have always been that way.

At ten I was engaging in fights with my brothers if they attempted to lord it over me. It's not that I was a tomboy. I simply could not accept that a girl could be considered inferior or less valuable than a boy. Or, even worse, a girl should be required to submit to masculine demands regardless of what she herself wanted. Yet the narrative reinforced in my world, was one where men and boys where privileged and their wishes, their views, and ways of doing things dominated everything. From these earliest of memories, I had a yearning for insurrection.

At sixteen I was even more conscious of these disparities. The resentment I felt, was amplified by the fact that I had four brothers and a multitude of male cousins. Everywhere I looked I could see the stark differences in how boys were treated; the opportunities and freedoms they were given compared to mine as a girl. Less was expected of them and yet their contributions more valued. And so, my instinct for equity and what was fair and just burned strongly.

In addition to this, my mother, whilst loving, was a patriarch at her core. Strict in her devotion to the view "that to be good, a woman must be selfless; and responsive to the needs and concerns of others", without a voice or desires of her own.[12] This meant I was at odds with almost everybody in my world. My views, my feelings and wishes were often dismissed or ignored. I was considered at best to be naïve, a young woman who did not understand how the world worked. At worst I was regarded as troublesome and difficult. Much of the time I felt alone and misunderstood. Yet, no matter how much pressure was placed on me to comply, the spirit within could not be quelled nor could the yearning for a fair, just, and humane world.[13]

Around this time, I made what I now consider to be an astonishing decision. With anger as a constant companion, I can remember thinking "I can't go on like this". It felt like my life was slowly being consumed by unhappiness. No matter how much I objected and

---

12 Carol Gilligan and David Richards, *Darkness Now Visible – Patriarchy's Resurgence and Feminist Resistance*, 2018, p 28.

13 Monica Sharma, *Radical Transformational Leadership – Strategic Action for Change Agents*, 2017, p 38.

pushed back, nothing changed.[14] I felt I was living a in world where I simply could not win[15] and so, with no other course of action open to me, I decided to bury my anger.

I had no idea that leaving my anger unexpressed and unacknowledged, whilst freeing me at one level, would be hugely problematic at another. At the time I was told by the adults around me that certain emotions were acceptable for a young woman to express, and others inappropriate. And if I continued to express these bad emotions no one would like me or want to have anything to do with me. At sixteen this seemed like a price too high to pay and so finally the controlling and manipulative claws of patriarchy silenced and shamed me into submission.

I have since learnt that when we have many experiences of not being heard, that these experiences mount up.[16] That at some point, when we've experienced a period of ongoing stress or we've simply had enough, we react in ways that can shock. These reactions are much like throwing kerosene onto an open fire that ignites an emotional explosion.[17] This has been true for me, my anger at times erupting seemingly out of nowhere. Yet, when I made this decision there was no one to reassure me that "it's OK to be angry".[18] And so, I did the only thing I could, I made the best choice available in the circumstance I found myself in.

---

14 Anodea Judith, *The Global Heart Awakens – Humanity's Rite of Passage from the Love of Power to the Power of Love,* 2013, p 259.

15 Carol Gilligan and David Richards, *Darkness Now Visible – Patriarchy's Resurgence and Feminist Resistance*, 2018, p 74.

16 Sarah Peyton, *Your Resonant Self, Guided Meditations and Exercises to Engage Your Brain's Capacity for Healing,* 2017, p 139.

17 Sarah Peyton, Your Resonant Self, *Guided Meditations and Exercises to Engage Your Brain's Capacity for Healing,* 2017, p 139.

18 Rebecca Campbell, *Rise Sister Rise – A Guide to Unleashing the Wise, Wild Woman Within, p 189.*

The understanding that feelings are neither good nor bad, and that it's OK to express them, was still to come.[19] The decision to bury my anger gave me the space to start thinking about what I wanted to create in my life rather than dwelling on what was unfair. Ironically, this desire to embrace my life as fully as I could eventually led me back to the need to accept my full self, including the 'good' and 'bad' emotions.[20]

This is not to say I stopped noticing the injustices or that I conceded to the view that men were superior. Boudicca's spirit was far too strong for that. I simply stopped giving voice to my dissatisfaction and pain. This, of course, meant I was muting the voice of my experience and silencing the outward expression of what I knew to be true.[21] Accordingly, my inner and outer worlds were at odds with each other. In the outer world I gave deference to the opinions of others and in my heart Boudicca's fierce, defiant, and bold spirit fuelled me.

The discord between my inner and outer worlds meant I was on constant guard. Continually testing how much of my true self I could reveal and how much I needed to keep under wraps. This in turn lead to a growing sense of uneasiness. A sense that I was always in enemy territory, never able to reveal my authentic self and never truly safe.

By the time I was twenty, my direction, my dreams and my hopes had been cut off and stifled again and again.[22] I may have only just been stepping into my life as an adult, but inside I was already a battle-weary warrior. Living with this level of repression, as any

---

19 Rebecca Campbell, *Rise Sister Rise – A Guide to Unleashing the Wise, Wild Woman Within, p 189.*

20 Susan David, *Emotional Agility – Get Unstuck, Embrace Change and Thrive in Work and Life,*2016, p 92.

21 Carol Gilligan and David Richards, *Darkness Now Visible – Patriarchy's Resurgence and Feminist Resistance,* 2018, p 27.

22 Clarissa Pinkola Estés, C. *Women Who Run with The Wolves – Contacting the Power of the Wild Woman,* 1993, p 365.

woman who has not fallen under the spell of patriarchy will tell you, can cause other gifts to arise that compensate and protect.[23]

Being battle weary, whilst exhausting, also kept me safe. I learnt to rely on my deepest knowing regardless of what I was told or how firmly something was reinforced. If a situation felt unsafe, like I needed to flee, then that was what I did. This inner knowing has kept me safe and protected me on many occasions. It has, for instance, saved me from being raped more than once. I've learnt, in a world ruled by patriarchal values, that often, "nothing is as it first seems"[24] and I've been compensated and protected by the sharpening of my intuition, instincts and abilities for "inner hearing, inner sensing and inner knowing".[25]

More than a single act of defiance.

I've also come to realise that the ability to be defiant is not a matter of rising to meet one infraction or setback as I thought as a young woman. To be adept and able to rise again and again with dignity and determination requires more than a single act of defiance and calls for vastly different ways of perceiving and responding.

In this quest, Boudicca's audacious spirit has guided me to fresh insights. I've found it particularly helpful to view patriarchy as a system rather than a personal assessment of my worthiness. In the past, I've often taken all these struggles personally and as a result have felt hounded, harassed, falsely imputed and less valued.[26] Yet, the reality is, patriarchy is a 5,000 year old system that is far more

---

23 Clarissa Pinkola Estés, C. *Women Who Run with The Wolves – Contacting the Power of the Wild Woman*, 1993, p 364.
24 Clarissa Pinkola Estés, C. *Women Who Run with The Wolves – Contacting the Power of the Wild Woman*, 1993, p 75.
25 Clarissa Pinkola Estés, C. *Women Who Run with The Wolves – Contacting the Power of the Wild Woman*, 1993, p 80-89.
26 Clarissa Pinkola Estés, C. *Women Who Run with The Wolves – Contacting the Power of the Wild Woman*, 1993, p 364.

insidious, pervasive, and persistent.[27] Viewed from this perspective, clearly, it's crazy to take these slights personally and if we do, we become victims to the system which then further hinders our ability to keep rising to the oppression of this hideous system. This understanding, of course, raises questions around how to keep rising in defiance.

I've started to appreciate that the patriarchal system, that at first glance seems to pit men and women against each other, is about power and not about gender at all. Boudicca's bold response to the abuse she and her daughters suffered is not about rising against the cruelty of men, although it was men inflicting the cruelty, she is rebelling against the brutality of Roman rule and fighting for loss of freedom.[28] Her personal suffering is an example of the cruelty and the lengths that patriarchy will go to maintain power.

The central organising principle behind the Roman Empire was one of divide and conquer.[29] For the Romans it was not enough to create "enemies where none existed" (to rationalise Rome's unjust wars). To be successful, they needed to divide their enemies from one another so that these enemies could not join forces and rise in opposition to Roman domination.[30] The divide and conquer principle, still alive today, plays out through the gender binary split, that separates and values the masculine over the feminine. This separation divides "intelligence (masculine) from emotions (feminine) and the self (masculine) from relationships (feminine)"[31] which in turn elevates the mind over the body and the self over

---

27 Anodea Judith, *The Global Heart Awakens – Humanity's Rite of Passage from the Love of Power to the Power of Love*, 2013, p 95.

28 Pruitt, Sarah. *"Who was Boudica?"*, History.com, 2016. http://historysheroes.e2bn.org/hero/whowerethey/2#More.

29 Carol Gilligan and David Richards, *Darkness Now Visible – Patriarchy's Resurgence and Feminist Resistance*, 2018, p 63.

30 Carol Gilligan and David Richards, *Darkness Now Visible – Patriarchy's Resurgence and Feminist Resistance,* 2018, p 63.

31 Carol Gilligan and David Richards, *Darkness Now Visible – Patriarchy's Resurgence and Feminist Resistance*, 2018, p 6.

relationships. This strategy that made it easier for the Romans to conquer and control their enemies compromises our ability to think about what we are feeling and our capacity to bring empathy and compassion together with logic to the solving of human problems.[32]

This separation "once viewed as signalling the achievement of rationality and personal autonomy" is now "recognised instead as the manifestations of injury and trauma".[33] As humans we are inherently relational and responsive beings with a deep desire and need to engage responsively with others.[34] This relational capacity is part of our evolutionary history and key to our survival as a species.[35] And so, the patriarchal system designed to divide, conquer and control not only impairs our capacity to see and repair the relationships that it has broken and shattered, it also hinders our capacity to love and feel empathy across these barriers.[36]

One of the most insidious aspects of the gender binary split is that it severely hinders our ability to fight back by shaming our capacity to resist.[37] In women, "shaming leads to the silencing of our voices, the very voices that might" reasonably enable us to "challenge the injustices of patriarchal demands".[38] And in men, shaming is linked

32 Carol Gilligan and David Richards, *Darkness Now Visible – Patriarchy's Resurgence and Feminist Resistance*, 2018, p 9, p64.

33 Carol Gilligan and David Richards, *Darkness Now Visible – Patriarchy's Resurgence and Feminist Resistance*, 2018, p 53.

34 Carol Gilligan and David Richards, *Darkness Now Visible – Patriarchy's Resurgence and Feminist Resistance*, 2018, p 3.

35 Carol Gilligan and David Richards, Darkness Now Visible – *Patriarchy's Resurgence and Feminist Resistance*, 2018, p 3.

36 Carol Gilligan and David Richards, *Darkness Now Visible – Patriarchy's Resurgence and Feminist Resistance*, 2018, p 63.

37 Carol Gilligan and David Richards, *Darkness Now Visible – Patriarchy's Resurgence and Feminist Resistance,* 2018, p 3.

38 Carol Gilligan and David Richards, *Darkness Now Visible – Patriarchy's Resurgence and Feminist Resistance*, 2018, p 45.

to men's anger and violence, and issues of honour, status and high sensitivity and reactivity to insult.[39]

Shaming generates in us a sense, not that we have done something bad, but that we are ourselves bad.[40] Thus, I've realised that we become conquered and controlled by our own shame, often feeling diminished and worthless in the process.[41]

With the dignity and determination of Boudicca's spirit as guidance, I'm reminded that this story of shame – that has been imprinted on us through patriarchal conditioning, tapping into all our self-doubts, fears, and our sense of failure – can also contain our hopes, dreams, aspirations, our full human capacities, and potential. Because as human beings "we are always the sum total of how and what we think of ourselves" and "the stories we tell ourselves about ourselves".[42] Boudicca's story reminds us that as painful as shaming is, it is something that "is imposed from the outside" whilst "courage, in contrast, comes from the inside".[43]

Armed with this knowledge I know that I too can choose to act courageously like Boudicca. And this choice is about knowing who I am and what I stand for – and when I can do that, I can come to life's choices with the most powerful tool of all: my full self.[44]

39 Carol Gilligan and David Richards, *Darkness Now Visible – Patriarchy's Resurgence and Feminist Resistance*, 2018, p 7, p 49.
40 Susan David, *Emotional Agility – Get Unstuck, Embrace Change and Thrive in Work and Life*, 2016, p 68.
41 Susan David, *Emotional Agility – Get Unstuck, Embrace Change and Thrive in Work and Life*, 2016, p 68.
42 Albert Flynn DeSilver, "*Writing as a path to Awakening*", 2017, p 130.
43 Harriet Lerner, *The Dance of Fear – Rising Above Anxiety, Fear and Shame to Be Your Best and Bravest Self*, 2005, p 220.
44 Susan David, *Emotional Agility – Get Unstuck, Embrace Change and Thrive in Work and Life*, 2016, p 130.

The audacity to belong.

Being infused with Boudicca's spirit has always meant that the drive toward wholeness would not let me be.[45] As a result, my life has been filled with acts of insubordination. This defiance is woven into everything – from my work as a leadership coach and organisational development specialist, to my commitment to heal my patriarchal wounds, to the types of relationships I have nurtured with others. My life's work has been devoted to strengthening and unifying our human capacity to connect, navigate and grow together in service to each other and the world at large. This has meant that my life choices have been completely at odds with a system aimed at dividing and separating; controlling and limiting us.

With Boudicca's audacious spirit as inspiration my ultimate defiance is having the audacity to choose to belong. I believe that the fact that you and I are here at all, is evidence that we have the right to be here, and a right to have our own voices and vision. Because in the end, you and I are products of and a consequence of creation itself.[46] And when we have the audacity to choose to belong – to belong to ourselves, to each other and to belong to humanity – it becomes easier to respond to all the challenges of patriarchy from a place of love. And love, "is based on equality and freedom".[47]

It will take love of the highest order to be courageous enough to call back our full power, to find our voices and unshackle our souls from the tyranny of 5,000 years of patriarchal oppression and wounding. I believe that Boudicca's audacious spirit calls me and you to stand with this level of courage in our lives. And I, for one, have found her voice cannot be denied – for she urges me to rise

---

45 Sherry Anderson & Patricia Hopkins, *The Feminine Face of God – The Unfolding of the Sacred in Women*, 1992, p 92.
46 Elizabeth Gilbert, *Big Magic – Creative living Beyond Fear*, 2015, p 96.
47 Carol Gilligan and David Richards, *Darkness Now Visible – Patriarchy's Resurgence and Feminist Resistance*, 2018, p 52.

again and again and to live with courage, dignity, and determination.

References

Anderson, S. & Hopkins, 1992, *The Feminine Face of God – The Unfolding of the Sacred in Women*, Bantam Books, New York.

Campbell, R. 2016, *Rise Sister Rise – A Guide to Unleashing the Wise, Wild Woman Within,* Hay House. www.hayhouse.com.au.

David, S. 2016, *Emotional Agility – Get Unstuck, Embrace Change and Thrive in Work and Life*, Penguin Random House, UK.

DeSilver, A.F. 2017, *"Writing as a path to Awakening",* Sounds True, Boulder, Colorado.

Forrest, S. 2010, *"The Inner Sky",* Seven Paws Press, Borrego Springs, CA.

Gilbert, E. 2015, *Big Magic – Creative living Beyond Fear,* Bloomsbury, London.

Gilligan, C. & Richards, D. 2018, *Darkness Now Visible – Patriarchy's Resurgence and Feminist Resistance,* Cambridge University Press, United Kingdom.

Judith, A. 2013, *The Global Heart Awakens – Humanity's Rite of Passage from the Love of Power to the Power of Love*, Shift Books, San Rafael, California.

Lerner, H. 2005, *The Dance of Fear – Rising Above Anxiety, Fear and Shame to Be Your Best and Bravest Self*, Harper, New York, USA.

Peyton, S. 2017, *Your Resonant Self, Guided Meditations and Exercises to Engage Your Brain's Capacity for Healing*, 2W.W. Norton & Company, New York.

Pinkola Estés, C. 1993, *Women Who Run with The Wolves – Contacting the Power of the Wild Woman*, Random House, London.

Pruitt, S. 2016, *"Who was Boudica?"*, History.com. http://historysheroes.e2bn.org/hero/whowerethey/2#More, Retrieved 31 January 2018.

Rein, V, 2019, *Patriarchy Stress Disorder – the invisible inner barrier to women's happiness and fulfillment*, Lioncrest Publishing, USA.

Sharma, M. 2017, *Radical Transformational Leadership – Strategic Action for Change Agents*, North Atlantic Books, Berkley, California.

Motherese
Lucy Pierce

Boudicca's Prayer on the Birth of Her First Daughter

Hayley Arrington

I have labored long
and I come to you now
with my prize, a daughter,
O, Invincible One!
My daughter,
newly born,
still wet with birth—
My limbs still stiff
from bracing and birthing.
O, Lady,
my daughter is my true Victory!
At the precipice, I cried your name—
I thank thee, Andraste, and call upon thee as woman speaking
to woman*
I have risen from childbed.
I will rise to motherhood
and anything else that comes my way
for I am under your protection
now and always.

*This line is a supposed quote of Boudicca's, from *Historia Romana* by Dio Cassius.

Defined by Our Defiance –
Taking up Boudicca's Fight
Pandora Le Cora

What do we do in the face of oppression? What do we let define us?

In this piece I am going to share with you some of my thoughts on the legendary Warrior Queen, Boudicca, and her role in both witchcraft and feminism, as well as some insights from my personal spiritual process. I trust that in picking up this book you would be aware that it contains themes of abuse, assault, mental illness, loneliness, heartbreak, oppression, subjugation, and disenfranchisement. It is your responsibility, dear reader, to be prepared to face these shadows with self-compassion and to maintain the self-care required to manage your own triggers. This essay also outlines some of my personal politics and it is my intention not to force my opinions on anyone, but to encourage you to simply consider them and ponder. I offer this piece to you in the hopes that reading about my process will help someone else with their own connection to Boudicca and the warrior queen archetype. I wish you enlightenment and healing on your own journey, as I have experienced on mine.

Boudicca was many things – a queen, a ruler, a political figure, a leader, a warrior, a military strategist, a mother, and a wife. She was also a rape survivor, a subject of conquest along with her kingdom and lands. She was widowed, beaten and subjugated, scorned and forced to witness the murder of her husband and sons and the rapes of her daughters. In the face of this oppression, Boudicca rose up and fought back in defiance of the invaders of her land and their callous acts. She led her army into eventual defeat. So many of us are also oppressed. We have also endured atrocities such as beatings, rapes, torture and attempts to break us (with varying levels of success). How can we look to the figure of Boudicca as a role model despite her defeat? How can we take up arms and continue her fight?

The word "feminism" has many meanings for many different people, and there are virtually limitless expressions of both feminist ideology and activism. To me feminism simply means fighting and standing up for the equal rights of girls and women, their liberation and their agency over their own bodies and lives. Such simple goals, but unattained in many cases even at the time of writing this in the year 2021.

The type of feminism I align most closely with is ecofeminism. Take care of your mother – you only have one. (I do not mean to invalidate the experience of those who have difficult relationships with their mothers... I myself do. I simply wish to impactfully assert that women and the earth are sacred and worthy of respect.) In my personal ecofeminist viewpoint, men are not seen as the enemy, but our brothers, fathers, friends. They can be our allies in the truest sense. They can certainly be victimised under what I call "the capitalist patriarchy" just as much as women can.

My feminism also includes transgender and non-gender conforming individuals, children and anyone who struggles under the current systems of extreme inequality and suppression of our rights – our rights to freedom, agency, choice, and safety. Fighting colonialism and upholding the rights of minorities and black, indigenous and people of colour is vital to intersectional feminism. So many have suffered oppression and deal with intergenerational trauma under a system that asserts that "might is right" and abuses its power for greed.

The capitalist patriarchy does not just consist of men, but rather refers to a system that affects us at all levels – our governments, the education system, the medical model, the media (which often promotes alarmism and fear) and our communities and society.

The earth, like women, is often exploited. Invaded. Seen as an object of conquest and domination. Raped even, and treated callously and carelessly. I do not wish to overly idealise the past, but in the time of Boudicca, the rulers of the British Isles (as those lands are called in modern times) were sworn to serve the people and the land. It was not about power for its own sake, empty displays of wealth and excess or "majesty", it was a sacred marriage with the land and with kin. Prior to the Industrial and Technological revolutions, humans lived in harmony with their natural landscapes. By many accounts, Boudicca carried out her duties and fulfilled her sacred purpose well. She is well deserving of her place in history and folklore as well as the place she holds in the hearts of many, including modern witches.

Boudicca as a figure in witchcraft can be seen and worked with in one's spiritual practice in a number of ways. As an historical figure her story captures the heart and imagination. As we consider her bravery in standing to fight against her oppressors, we can find the bravery within ourselves to stand up for what is right and fair. We consider how she kept going despite the trauma she endured, and we find the strength to keep going in the face of our trials. Even this is a powerful form of magic in and of itself. Some would call it shadow work. As we face our fears, our shame and everything we have denied ourselves and buried from our past we can heal and grow. Simply knowing of a woman and warrior queen such as Boudicca is a powerful reminder of the resilience and tenacity we are capable of. She can also of course be worked with and invoked in rituals, spells, and magical work. Like some other historical figures, such as Joan of Arc, she can be worshipped as a goddess.

My first personal encounter with the figure of Boudicca in the context of my witchcraft practice happened around 2018. I heard the song "Boudica" by the singer Karliene. The words and music touched me deeply and spoke to my very heart and soul. I thought about everything Boudicca went through and how she got up, beaten and bloody, ready to fight to her death. Unwilling to give up her position, dignity, and sovereignty without a fight. At this point in my life, I was struggling profoundly with mental illness and new motherhood, and I suddenly understood that my pain was the result of trauma and a long-standing pattern of not standing up to fight on my own behalf. I also read a book called *The Body Keeps Score* by Dutch psychiatrist Bessel Van Der Kolk, and I realised that my body had indeed kept score of trauma, affecting my nervous system and raising my baseline level of stress and anxiety. Amnesiac walls broke down and I remembered when I was groomed and raped when I was underage, and how painful and traumatic it truly was. I finally owned up to myself about how much it had affected me at the time, and continued to affect me.

Shortly following this I attended the funeral of a beloved family member and had to travel through the town where my rapist lived. Something snapped. I realised enough was enough and I had to stand up for myself. I had to admit to myself why I wasn't OK and begin to let go of the shame I carried (a process that continues still). I also had to stand up for so many others who had been through something similar (as well as those who were at risk of going through a similar ordeal). This experience was compounded by the birth of my second child, a daughter, and the fear of what she could endure in her life. I am told that this is common for women survivors who parent girls, as we are better able to relate our lived experience to what we hope and fear for our daughters. I finally stopped pretending I was ten feet tall and bulletproof and began to take stock of the damage.

When we are born into, or later find ourselves in oppressive environments and situations we are so often conditioned to take it lying down. We are expected to roll over and just give up. We are taught that we deserve it. We learn that standing up for ourselves is a losing battle. Why fight a losing battle? I remind you that Boudicca did just that.

In witchcraft, many witches relate to the concept of the maiden mother and crone, three connected goddess figures that relate to the life stages of women. These figures are all valued and devalued in their own ways, and by considering this in our shadow work we can gain powerful insights and strength. The mother is valued as a nurturer and provider. She is devalued when she is exploited and over-taxed... criticised for her imperfections. Those of her post-partum body, her mothering style and how she chooses to parent her children and live her life (to name but a few). Many mothers are chronically under-supported and taken advantage of in their family and community. I have experienced this personally. I have also had the experience of feeling devalued in the maiden aspect of my life.

The maiden is often valued too highly for her sexuality and is objectified when she should be personified. Around the time that Boudicca came onto my path I also heard a very powerful poem called "Little Girls Don't Stay Little Forever" by English poet Erin May Kelly. This poem hit me like a brick. I was reminded of the way girls and their interests are mocked; their deep inner worlds dismissed. How this often goes hand in hand with violation, abuse, and oppression. Again, I was triggered. Awakened. Made painfully aware of my own trauma and the damaged inflicted on my body and psyche. All of these triggers proved necessary for my healing. After years of feeling ashamed of what had happened to me, I felt angry. I finally realised it wasn't my fault.

Anyone who has experienced grooming knows how insidious it is – how trust is built and small boundaries are violated at first before that trust is betrayed. Once the rape had happened, I felt as though I could hardly tell up from down and was so confused about what had happened to me. I thought it was my own fault because I had "let" it happen, when really, I should never have been put in that position. He told me that I could not leave him with "blue balls", that I could not say "stop" once he had started. I didn't know any better, due to a lack of both education and self-esteem. So, I went through an ordeal of around 1 hour. He predictably dropped me like a hot rock afterwards (which was a relief) and told people. I was bullied and slut-shamed, and only worried what would happen to me if more people found out. It was a difficult, lonely, and stressful time in my life. I was 13. Going through all of this at such a tender and impressionable age was unfortunately no small part of what I let define me in my formative years.

I realise that what I went through is not as horrific as the ordeals endured by others, but I have also learned that I must validate myself. It was one of the most painful and degrading experiences of my life. By denying and suppressing it I only made myself sicker and sicker as the years went by. It was years before I knew the signs of trauma and gained insight into the root of my anxiety, depression, feelings of worthlessness, dissociation, and many other manifestations of mental illness.

Upon these realisations, I took action. I made a belated #metoo social media post (2 years after the hashtag began trending). I told people about my experience and talked at length to both counsellors and trusted friends. I wrote a letter to my rapist (and yes, I sent it). It wasn't an easy time in my life, but in doing these things I felt that I had finally stood up for both myself and other survivors of grooming and assault.

In January of 2021, Grace Tame was named Australian of the year for her work in advocacy, changing laws and raising awareness of sexual abuse and assault. This was both triggering and vindicating for me and many other survivors of abuse, assault, and grooming. At the age of 15, Grace was groomed and repeatedly raped by a 58-year-old teacher. He was charged and convicted of his crimes, however because of bullying and slut-shaming she had to change schools. As a result of the successful #letherspeak social media campaign, gag-laws preventing survivors of convicted crimes from identifying themselves were overturned. Grace was allowed to tell

87

her side of her story. When the grooming and abuse took place Grace was a vulnerable teen who was anorexic, mentally ill, seeing a therapist and having problems at home. Her perpetrator became a close confidant to her before taking advantage of the situation and his position to violate her. After he was convicted, her attacker bragged about his crimes on social media, saying that having a "relationship" with a 15-year-old girl was "awesome" and that many men envied him. Stories like this are all too common. The vulnerable need to be protected. Attitudes need to change along with laws. The type of work Grace does is imperative. It protects vulnerable people, and it also heals.

A major breakthrough occurred in 2018 when I began attending a therapeutic art group once every week for three months. Having this time and space to sit down and make art was immensely healing and transformative. My pieces of art flowed out of me like pus... and I do apologise for the analogy, but that is how healing and essential the process was. To this day I continue to make art. The mindful flow state is soothing to my nervous system. It makes me a happier and less stressed person.

Another source of vicarious catharsis was in 2019, when Australian witch and rap artist Zheani (who holds the distinction of being the originator of the "fairy trap" genre) released her song "The Question", in which she spoke of her experience of being trafficked and abused by a famous rapper. Hearing this young woman roar and rap words such as "this ain't no me too b*tch/this is beef/and I'll beat you for the way you treated me/I'll expose and defeat you" and "I never told what happened 'cos the fear of disbelief/for years my brain could not conceive what happened to me" with such strength and fury was incredibly healing. Knowing you are not alone in having had such an experience is powerful, albeit devastating. Zheani's story is harrowing, and yet by telling her story through her art she has helped many. After releasing "The Question", Zheani was sent a cease-and-desist letter by the rapper's lawyer, and the song was removed from all major streaming platforms. It remains uploaded to her YouTube channel at the time I am writing this. She also released it on a double-sided vinyl record of her EP's "The Line" and "Satanic Prostitute". Satanic Prostitute was a slur levelled at her by her enemies, which she reclaimed as a term of empowerment despite those who hated and disbelieved her. "Witch", "bitch", "slut", "whore", "faggot"... all of these slurs are commonly reclaimed in the feminist movement as an act of taking back our power.

The woman in the crone stage of life is also devalued, when she should be revered for her invaluable experience and wisdom. Perhaps I will experience this firsthand one day. Perhaps you will, or already have. Older women are often mocked for their supposed lack of sexual desirability. And yet rape is not about sex, but rather power and control. Rapists either feel entitled to sex or crave the power to take away a woman's choice and control (or both). As such, many older women have had to stand up and tell their stories to police and the courts – playing their own important roles in taking up Boudicca's fight against those who violate women. In the time of Boudicca, to rape a queen was to violate not only her, but the entire domain over which she ruled – her kingdom, people, and lands. When we know we stand for something important, it is worth continuing Boudicca's fight. Peace, love, health, pleasure, freedom, choice, and the sanctity of our inner and outer worlds are all things worthy of going into the bloodiest of battles for.

I write this because I believe we can stand against our oppressors by looking to the figure of Boudicca as an ancestor and spirit ally, a role model and even a goddess. Our activism and our voice can be used sacredly to stand up for the rights of all oppressed people (and all the earth's creatures that make up our ecosystem).

Remember also that centering your activism on promoting the interests and rights of yourself (and the demographics and groups you are a part of) can be an act of self-care. Self-awareness is key to knowing where to put your energy. You may engage in small acts at home such as reducing, reusing, and recycling. You could get involved in organisations that align with your values, volunteer your time, and join protests. Speaking for yourself and your interests (especially in online spaces) can be seen as "slacktivism", but it too is vital. Be mindful to also back up your words with real life action. Activism does not begin and end with virtue signalling. You can vote with your feet, your wallet, and your actual democratic vote when this is available to you. If you are a mother, raise children who are kind and responsible – who will respect women and the earth, stand against oppression and fight for justice. Demonstrate kindness and respect, especially by being kind and respectful towards the children themselves. Provide them with a safe environment to share their thoughts, dreams, and experiences with you. Teach them they are deserving of love, safety, respect, freedom, agency, choice, prosperity, and life satisfaction. Remember that you yourself are deserving of these things. All sentient beings are. Ending the cycles of hate crimes, bigotry and rape culture begins with education, and education begins at home. So many of us just think we want what we are conditioned to want by society and our early home environments. The picket fence, the 2.5 kids, certain brands of clothing and models of cars... what do we really want and need? Asking ourselves this question, deconstructing the conditioning of the capitalist construct, and getting to the root of what we really need and want as humans is imperative to both the path of the witch and our survival as a species.

With all the existential threats and crises we currently face, it is impossible to know what the future truly holds, especially now that we live in the time of the global corona virus pandemic (at the time of writing). I personally think it is unwise to be either too optimistic or too pessimistic. I choose to focus on the potential of this world and to have hope. From what I can perceive, many people on the planet at this time are going through what I would describe as an awakening, and as a result they are choosing to engage in different ways of living. Off grid living, zero waste, minimalism, simplified living, the development of environmentally friendly technology as well as clean forms of energy, growing their own food, homesteading, permaculture, conscious ways of being in relationships, mindful parenting, gentle parenting, more effective methods of communication, radical honesty, ethical polyamory, reducing the consumption of finite resources, veganism and eating natural foods... I could go on. These practices (which often go against the grain and the current norm of living off the earth and Her creatures instead of living in sacred relationship with Her) could change the world for the better. They could bring about a collective evolution and bring us closer to attaining everything Boudicca fought for. The main problem I see is not apathy as many would argue, but that many of these lifestyle factors are accessible only to those with significant wealth and educational privilege. This access to resources and life changing information and life skills is yet another thing for which we must fight. Capitalism feeds off the promotion of a lack mentality – the idea that there is not enough to go around, and that is why most of the world's wealth is held by only 1% of the population while the vast majority of humans on this planet live in poverty. In truth there is enough for everyone's need but not everyone's greed. I do not claim to have all the answers to fix this situation, especially when I know that many do not have the option to adopt the aforementioned lifestyle choices. We can each only do our best with what we have available to us. I do believe that by grounding into our connectedness with the earth and loving relationships with one another, we recognise what really matters, we honour the sacred and we combat capitalistic greed.

In the fight against oppression, I want to emphasise the importance of self-care once again as well as the maintenance of our own personal spiritual and healing paths. I really cannot reiterate enough that you and your wholeness and wellness, are important in this fight. The concept of self-care came about through the fight for black rights. It is more than salt baths and mud masks for working mothers (although it can include this), it is any and every act that prioritises our sacred selves. Rest. Eating well. Keeping the body strong through movement. Spending restorative time in nature. Maintaining strong boundaries and saying no to unnecessary and unimportant drains on our time and energy. Prioritising nurturing relationships. Limiting time spent with those who do not support us or want the best for us. I would strongly suggest that you not take lovers who belittle, berate and body shame you. The people we choose to keep around us can make or break us. Secure, loving and trusting relationships are healing to our nervous systems. Feeling a sense of belonging is transformative in our lives. Make a commitment to seeking and maintaining these loving companionships with both friends and lovers. If you grew up in an environment where these connections were not present, you may need to seek professional help to learn how to build them.

There is no shame in this. Not all of us grow up in healthy environments, and healthy relationships take work. Choose also to prioritise spending time with those who share your values. We do not need to agree about everything, but we do need to agree on taking a strong stand together against bigotry and oppression. We can be allies to each other in Boudicca's fight.

Make time for the hobbies, interests and activities that light us up and fill us with joy. Keep making art! Visual art, handicrafts, poetry, song. and the written word are healing because they allow us to express ourselves. Being "in the zone" whilst creating is also a mindful state and getting into this state is so important to our healing. As witches, we also enter this zone when we practice magic and ritual work. It is important however to also take our magical energy and effort out of the circle and into our real lives. Magic is there to augment and support our real-world actions, and when we use them together, we are incredibly powerful. And true power is about having choice and control over self.

We do not have to be perfect (perfection being a human concept anyway), sometimes we will falter and make mistakes that don't support our goals and growth. We fall into ruts, abusing foods and substances, choosing the couch instead of the forest walk, texting that person who doesn't value us, and failing to save money and make time for what truly matters to us. I would know, I fell into one of these ruts recently myself. We do have the power to change our habits, and more beneficial behaviours can become second nature, giving us the strength to forge ahead. I have had my trials and challenges, and they have caused damage, but I choose to stand and fight. To prioritise myself and my mental health recovery. I didn't deserve what happened to me – nobody does. Like every aware and sentient being I deserve love, joy, happiness, pleasure, comfort, prosperity, success, and a sense of meaning and purpose in my life. My wounding and trauma are not my fault, but they are my responsibility. Only I can take the steps towards having a life worth living. Without self-love, self-compassion, self-care, self-kindness, and self-acceptance we perish. With them we thrive.

In my current day job as a support worker in the disability and mental health fields I help facilitate personal development and independent living groups for young people with disabilities (including autism spectrum conditions). This group is particularly vulnerable to grooming and abuse. I hope to teach them the skills to be safe. I hope to teach them that their worth is inherent. As a survivor it feels good to be doing my small part. All of us can contribute to the kind of world we want to be a part of; the kind of world that Boudicca fought for. Perhaps in your own way you already are.

So, what do we let define us? Are we defined by our trauma, damage, wounding, the barbs and jibes directed at us by others? Or are we defined by our defiance in standing up and fighting against our oppressors? Do we give in, roll over and accept a life of subjugation and smallness? Or do we look to the figure of

93

Boudicca for inspiration, and channel our rage and fury into fighting for all that is ours by right? We can be an army of scorned, scarred survivors fighting for our sacred land and kin. It is my hope that as many warriors as possible will take up spiritual arms. Boudicca lost her final battle. But we, her descendants of blood and spirit, can use every weapon at our disposal and win her war.

Bibliography

Van Der Kolk, B. *The Body Keeps Score – Brain, Mind and Body in the Healing of Trauma*. New York, Penguin Books, 2015.

Songs and Poems Referenced:

"Boudicca" by Karliene

"Little Girls Don't Stay Little Forever" by Erin May Kelly

"The Question" by Zheani

Boudicca
Arlene Bailey

She Walks the Land Remembering

Arlene Bailey

In the stillness of the night
you can hear her calling
Like a wraith raised from the dead,
her bloody sword held high,
she walks the land

Stripped of her title, her King
and Consort murdered,
daughters violated, this Queen
walks that which once held
her and her family, the land
that once held the great
Tribe of the Iceni

She walks remembering...

Before Rome came claiming
ownership as the new rulers
of the place she'd called home,
the place her ancestors called home
before the conqueror came bringing
oppression to all she held dear

Remembering...

When the land held her and her family
giving them all that they needed
The same land that flowed red
with the blood of the conqueror,
The land that flowed red with
the blood of her brave tribe
The Iceni now only a memory

Remembering...

How they beat her and raped her daughters
The rage she felt and the conviction that
she had lived on her own terms,
fought on her own terms,
and By Goddess,
she would die on her own terms

But first she would lay waste
to all they held precious, to
their sons and daughters,
their beloveds, their precious
Londinium, usurped and raped
of all former cultural ways
and traditions of the Britons,
Now a prize of the oppressors

She laughed as she watched
this now Roman city burn,
cursing their kind for laying
waste to all that she knew,
all she had known

Laughed as she laid waste to the
mighty Roman Army, the invaders,
their legions fearing her as they
heard her blood-curdling cry and
felt the pierce of her sword

Nothing left in the end but
the myths of her time
and the story of the
Warrior Queen of the Iceni

Nothing left but the nights
she walks the land, seeing
the battles in her mind,
the blood flowing

Her sword held high as
she holds the reins of the
horses, driving her chariot
toward the battle for
Sovereignty and Dignity

Her daughters beside her,
fighting for the ways of the Iceni,
fighting for the ways of all Celtic
tribes and indeed all of Briton,
she willingly offered her life knowing
she would never submit to
Roman occupation or oppression

Knowing that the conquerors did
not win, for they could not catch her,
nor find her or her daughters to
torture and then parade about
as some prize for all to see

She walks the land knowing,
Remembering that she stood
her ground fighting to protect
what was hers,
fighting to end oppression,
standing always in her
sovereignty and power
and, yet, wondering...

What did it all matter?

Did it matter?

Does anyone even know or
remember her name?

~*~*~*~*~

Ahhhh, Yes, Boudicca,
Queen of the Iceni,
You ARE remembered
Your heroic actions held
in the annals of time
Your story told over and over

The story of the woman
who became the Legend,
the story of Boudicca,
Warrior Queen of the Iceni

You who once brought together
the disparate tribes of the Celts,
harnessing their power as
you created an army so fierce
that your very name drove fear
into the Romans

You who now comes to us from
beyond the Veil whenever we call,
with sword in hand offering whatever
we need to battle oppression and
stand in the sovereignty of the self

You who offers up the call of battle
for the displaced, the disparate,
the ones who stand against tyranny
and oppression at all costs

We, the women far from your time,
Remember!

We, the women in our time,
Fight!

And

We the women of the now,
standing strong, our battle cry
heard far and wide,
will never, ever, Surrender!

So Rest Well Warrior Queen
for the world does indeed know
your story and as we stand in
Sovereignty, raising our swords
against the oppressors, our cry will
always be...

Hail the Warrior Queen of the
Great Tribe of the Iceni,
She with mighty sword and
Blood-curdling cry,

Hail Boudicca!

Hail Boudicca!

Hail Boudicca!

To you, great Warrior Queen,
we remember and we bow.

_____

Arlene Bailey, ©2021

Rage of a Woman

Arlene Bailey

Boudicca Rises

Arlene Bailey

In 2018, when Brett Kavanaugh was nominated to the Supreme Court of the United States and there were accusations of rape that surrounded the confirmation hearings, a voice began coming to me. She was outraged and there would be times she would scream at me to not let this happen again. She was in my dreams and my waking consciousness and all she kept saying was *Do not let them rape my daughters again*. We had lots of conversations about this issue, about *Him* and why She was so angry. Finally, one day She said...

OK, now that I have your attention and know your heart and mind, you may now know mine. I am Boudicca, Queen of the Iceni and I know that you already know my story. What you don't know is that throughout history it... Patriarchy... has come again and again and destroyed our ways of peaceful living and our social structure that honored women. Again and again, my daughters have been raped and those responsible always walk away with no consequences. Now, it's happening again and this time I have chosen you to be my voice.

I have to admit I was stunned. Of course, I knew who She was. What I didn't know was what I was supposed to do about what was happening. What could I, one woman, do?

Then one day I saw a political cartoon referring to the travesty that was the treatment of Christine Blasey Ford by the men hearing testimony at Kavanaugh's confirmation. Ms. Ford had come forward accusing Kavanaugh of rape and no one was listening to her. Even worse was the fact that they were making her out to be the villain. The image showed Lady Justice blindfolded, her scales askew, with the hands of one man covering her mouth and the other gripping her wrist holding her down. I felt a rage I'd never known rise from the depths of the annals of History and how HERstory had always been revised and rewritten. From deep within my very being, I felt a guttural scream of *NEVER AGAIN*. Still, I was not sure what one woman could do.

Then I heard... *WRITE*! Use the power of your words! Don't let Christine Blasey Ford and the others stand alone while one more male walks away free from any responsibility for rape.

Boudicca Rises

Many would not agree with the sharing of the image of the assault on Lady Justice. Most will not *Like* it. Still, I feel called to reference it for it speaks a powerful truth that most of us want to ignore and pretend is not happening. For days I've been sick – literally – from the collective energy surrounding the current attack on women. Sure, I could call it Supreme Court confirmation hearings, but in truth it is the ultimate assault on women and women's rights. **We. Do. Not. Matter.** Not just in the grand scheme of this hearing, but – to these men – we do not matter at all. We are merely an impediment meant to be stomped on, an irritant to shackle and control, if not completely eradicate.

AND...

Women ARE Rising. I know this. I see this. Sadly, though, as long as these *old white men* have the power they have and the monetary support that holds them in place, our battle is far from over. In fact, it has actually just become HUGE. As women we HAVE come a long way in changing things, but if we think our fight is over or less, then we are not paying attention. It's about to get a whole lot worse.

AND...

As I've read in many places, Patriarchy has just awakened the Sleeping Dragon... Kali... Lilith... the Morrigan... the Amazon. By their callous disregard of women and women's lives and safety, they have called forth Boudicca, the Iceni Queen who raged against the Romans who killed her husband and raped her daughters. Just. Because. They. Could. Sound familiar?

Once again white male invaders are raping women and setting in gold policies that control who and what can control a woman's body. Again...

103

Just Because They Can. Such a familiar ring to this mindset that keeps circling back again and again and again

BUT...

The women of today will not tolerate this behavior and have raised their banner and their arms.

Now, each of us is reaching our tipping point.

For me, it was a few days ago. It began as a hack of my Facebook account and the need to change my password. I hate having to change my password because it can never be like any other and so there are millions of words and combinations floating around out there that I'm supposed to remember. FTS! I was irritated that some sleaze bag had hacked accounts and now I was inconvenienced by such an irritant.

Though this stupid, inconsequential act was *my* tipping point, what I was REALLY angry about was what was happening with Christine Blasey Ford and Brett Kavanaugh... how they were crucifying her while simultaneously sanctifying him. I was angry that I'd been raped in college and no one did one single thing about it. There was no justice, no punishment for the preacher's kid who assaulted me never admitting guilt or showing any remorse. I was so angry that I was just one more statistic and, having to once again watch this scenario play out, I could feel a fierce rage rising within. But it was not just my rage...

As I kept thinking and raging about the stupid password mess, what really filled me with rage was all the insidiousness happening to women in this moment and what or, rather who, kept coming to mind was Boudicca. I kept thinking about what she'd do. The only words that made any sense in my cluttered mind – the only ones clear – were **BOUDICCA RISES**. So, I thought about making that my password, but then words began to come and I knew that phrase was bigger than a mere password. In truth, though, it did open something for me.

Like a raith raised from a haunted rest, Boudicca would not go away... her sword cutting through all the thoughts, all the feelings, all the bullshit until she had my attention, my tears, my rage, my full-bodied attention. Every hair on my arms, my hair... raised like antennas sensing, feeling. Words pulsing through my brain like an emotional hurricane until I knew what was coming. Knew what was birthing. She. SHE. Boudicca. The raging Queen of the Iceni was rising through me and she would have her say... have her wrath expressed... on the page... on the canvas.

But first the tears had to flow and words had to flow outward into the void...

I write with a broken heart, though I do not know why. I have good things in my life, good people. Some of both really good. Then why do I feel this rage building and my heart cracking wide open?

Why do I feel lower than the lowest worm? Why do I not matter? Why am I scorned and spit at and revolting to so many?

It is because I, a woman, exist. Not that I exist here or there, but that I simply exist.

Why did I choose to come to this time, this fucking time, as a woman. Have I not been ridiculed enough in previous lifetimes? Have I not been murdered and tortured, burned and buried alive before? Why risk that again?

There is a primal scream in me this time. A primal rising that says NO MORE!

All I hear in my soul is BOUDICCA RISES!

And so SHE comes... Sword in hand with a death scream that rents the very fabric of the cosmos.

Patriarchy came for my daughters once... had its way with them and then tossed them aside... killed my beloved and took my crown. Well, not this time. Not as long as my hands hold a sword and my voice speaks. Not as long as women continue to wake up – really pay attention – and use their voices.

Make no mistake, we are at war – not just for the soul of this current woman accusing a powerful man of rape, but for the soul of every woman, every girl on this planet, including Mother Earth herself.

We are at war and it is going to take commitment from every woman, every girl, every man who stands with us. It's going to take reaching our *tipping point* and hearing that guttural scream in our very soul.

It's going to take...

Each individual who will commit to the idea of NOT ON MY WATCH...

Each woman who will stand and shout...

I AM WOMAN.

I WILL BE SEEN.

I WILL BE HEARD.

I walk with Boudicca, Queen of the Iceni and I WILL have my justice, my revenge.

Listen... can you hear the rage of woman? My rage? Your rage?

Listen as you hear the call come from across the centuries, see the Queen dripping in blood as she risks everything for truth and justice as she unites all the tribes for the sole purpose of eradicating the oppressor and reclaiming sovereignty.

Like a raith rising, Queen Boudicca, sword in hand, waits for the women of today to rise and take their revenge on the oppressor. She waits for the women of today to find their voice and the guttural scream of sovereign power!

I have had my tipping point.

Where... what... is yours Sister?

Listen...

Boudicca Rises by Arlene Bailey, © 2018, 2021

Originally published in *She Summons: Why Goddess Feminism, Activism and Spirituality? Volume 1* – edited by Kaalii Cargill and Helen Hye-Sook Hwang. Mago Books, 2021.

O Sovereign Holy

Iris Eve

O Sovereign Holy,
She of No Masters,
Revered Mother Warrior,
Protectress of the Old Ways,
Queen Boudicca the steadfast;

You who stands vigilant
in defiance of oppression,
in the face of sanctioned brutality,
we honor you.

You, who with more courage
than ten thousand Roman soldiers,
stared down a threat the size of militarized religion,
and still came roaring bravely into battle,
dauntless in your defense of the sacred,
we thank you.

So fierce was your fortitude
that even after your foes
destroyed all you held dear,
and burnt everything to the ground,
still they committed your feats
to their own history books.

Chronicled by your enemies
as a formidable warrior indeed,
but also as a woman of strange magic.

So fearsome was your campaign,
so cunning was your power,
your legacy of resistance lives on
in the hearts of your descendants
as our birthright,
and we revere you.

Born of the greatest violation,
into the ashes of a defeated nation,
your granddaughters rise.

Boudicca

Andrea Redmond

The Story of Woman

Tamara Albanna

Boudicca was never a figure I knew intimately.

I have heard her name. I learned that she is known for her bravery and sacrifice. I also know that even though her story is an older one—it lives on today in women all over the world.

I felt her fierceness deeply very recently, when the Taliban swept through Afghanistan once more, and we saw the images of people, mostly men, trying to flee.

I then saw images of Afghani women, heavily armed and vowing to protect their country.

I was reminded of homeland, Iraq, where there were similar scenes of women fighting against Daesh, to push them out of their country.

Men come to rape, pillage, and destroy.

Then they flee.

Women hold the earth, hold their children, and fight.

Women sacrifice, pay the ultimate price, to fight and protect what is theirs.

Boudicca took her life in honor, rather than succumb to the hands of the aggressor.

Women in Syria and Iraq committed suicide, rather than fall into the hands of Daesh and a fate worse than death.

How can this be seen as anything other than the ultimate power, the ultimate show of autonomy?

We die on our own terms, we die with honor, we die fighting.

We are not the victims the media likes to show. Far from it.

By telling the story of Boudicca, we are telling the story of women today. The women who carry her spirit. Of justice, autonomy, and liberation.

We tell Her story; we tell the story of Woman.

Boudicca and the Hare

Emma Clark

When she released that hare from the folds of her dress,
Men held their breath in the still of morning,
Before their cheers resounded across the landscape.
Running on the right side for battle
She is still moving through history
Hind legs grazing the bare earth,
Showing the way for what will come.
The invaders built straight roads
But her way was not always so certain.
Her path was veering, oscillating,
In the diffused light of dawn and dusk
She outwitted her pursuers in the twist of divinatory fate.
What other fierce magic was unleashed from the darkness of her
womanhood?
At the meeting-place when all is in balance,
At the tipping point,
At the equinox of souls,
She is the disruptor, the defiant one,
The protector of daughters,
The fire that will not be contained.
Her name is a scorched scar of memory,
Like Londinium's charred layer of earth.
When all is burning like the stubble of a harvest field,
When the world is changing,
And in the searing heat of oppression,
The hare rises from the hot earth,
And leaps through flame,
Guiding the way for She who would stand
Against an empire.

The Face of Defiance

Sionainn McLean

"LOL! But she died, what was the point?"

Every time there is a discussion somewhere on Boudicca, I see words similar to this. I can't help but feel incredulous and angry.

> Cu Chulainn.
>
> Achilles.
>
> Spartacus.
>
> Leonidas I.
>
> Tlahuicole.
>
> Ragnar Lothbrook.
>
> Galvarino.
>
> William Wallace.

To name a few.

Few men ever say "but they died, what was the point" about these "heroes" because they were men, standing up for what they believed in, fighting for their cause, facing their deaths proudly.

So why do they shake their heads at Boudicca's story? She died like her male counterparts, a message to the world in her actions – It was better to die fighting than it was to live on your knees.

It's almost as if women are held to a different standard. Men can live and die by the sword – avenging injustice, claiming what's "theirs," and fighting for what they believe in. For these men, few ever laugh and say, "but they died," as if victory is only ever measured by staying alive.

But when the topic of Boudicca is raised, that's what I hear them do. The fact is that after her husband died, after her lands were stolen, after she was publicly whipped and after her daughters were raped, she picked up a spear and shield, and led her army to battle. She destroyed Camulodunum and burned Londinium and Verulamium, killing 70,000–80,000 in her wrath. Does that mean nothing, simply because she was a woman?

We women have the heart of a warrior, the soul of a mama bear protecting her cubs. Inside each of us is a piece of Boudicca. But when we are children, society tries to stamp it out.

> Be Ladies.
>
> Sugar and spice and everything nice.
>
> Don't swear.
>
> Girls cry so easily.
>
> Why are you so emotional? Is it that time of the month?
>
> Don't get muddy and dirty, girls are clean creatures.
>
> Don't shout.
>
> Don't learn to fight, or use weapons, or shoot big guns (Though sometimes you can carry this cute little camo pink gun, just in case you are foolish enough to put yourself in a situation where you could get robbed or raped.)
>
> Don't get raped.
>
> Go to college to get your degree, but don't make more money than your potential husband.
>
> Be slim and fit, but not so you can fight. Do it so you look great on a man's arm.
>
> Die as an old widow, content with your children and grandchildren, tame and peaceful.

Our piece of Boudicca never gets stamped out though, it's just pushed inside us, deep and forgotten. Sometimes a piece shines through, when we need to protect our children, our loved ones, even our homes, but in the end, society makes us push it back. Be tamed, Boudicca. You should've rolled over to the Romans.

Had it been her husband Prasutagus, would these same men be jeering the man that he avenged his wife and daughters by burning cities? Would they dismiss the fact that he fought to the end to protect his people from slavery, a fate many might consider worse than death? Or would they lift his name in awe and consider him someone to emulate, a true hero to look up to? Of course they would. He would've died a hero, sword in hand, fighting for honorable reasons: justice, freedom, defiance.

I look at the story of Boudicca, and I wonder what she was like before the Romans came along. I bet she was a strong-willed child who got dirty, who played against the boys, training in case she ever needed to fight. I bet she was a generous lover to her husband, and she loved her daughters more than life itself.

I bet she laughed a lot, and enjoyed the beautiful warm days, and found meaning in the cold dark days. I wonder if she howled at the moon, in a moment of sheer bliss for her untamed, wild self, her unrestrained emotions and desires. I bet she worshipped strong Gods, and when her world shattered, I wonder if she had a moment of weakness, and asked why? Why her? Why her children, why her husband?

Boudicca, in her grief, might've realized that the Roman army itself was enormous, and what could one person do? The Gods don't grant wishes, they only give us the means to chase them. Did Andraste hand Boudicca her spear and tell her to fight, to extract her vengeance where she could? Maybe she knew it was a lost cause but chose to fight nonetheless. Because in the end, she knew her people would die anyway – either as slaves to the Romans, or as free people.

And her vengeance she had. She wiped out everyone at Camulodunum, and then burned the cities of Londinium and Verulamium. Her armies showed no mercy, just as the Romans had shown no mercy to her or her daughters. Her wrath was so strong that Nero himself almost gave up, almost withdrawing his troops from Briton.

However, it was not meant to be. The Iceni were not equipped for the last battle against Suetonius and his men, and perhaps Boudicca and her generals got too arrogant, after so many victories. We can never know why it befell as it did that day, only that it did, with Boudicca's fate being death by her own hands. I choose to believe a woman so determined to defy Rome would rather have taken her own life rather than give them the satisfaction of taking her alive. To say she died in any other way was only to minimize her impact and shame her.

But Boudicca was as brave, if not braver than any man. She was... she IS the face of defiance against oppression, someone whose name should be on the lips of our daughters and sons. Boudicca, guided by Andraste, had her revenge against the wrongs Rome inflicted upon her and her people. May we learn from her strength, and her mistakes, and when faced with oppression, invoke her presence so our spears land true. So that we understand that some things are worth fighting for, and all fights have a risk of death. We should not back away from those fights because we are afraid.

Defiance

Karen Storminger

Boudicca
You refused to bend
So they tried to break you
You rose from the pain they inflicted
Stood tall, sword in hand
Claiming what was yours by right

I stood, battle ready
With my words, I claimed what was mine
I heard the haughty, condescending laughter
I saw the contempt staring back at me
Laughing behind icy eyes
Then I watched, feet firmly planted
I watched the darkness snap its tether at my defiance
Rage, released
Lunging in a moments frenzy
Wall at my back
Elbow at my throat
Fist poised to strike
I meet my enemy eye to eye
No longer afraid
Calm, steady, anger coursing through my veins
I speak the words he never thought to hear
Watch lover turned tormentor falter
Hesitate, step back, defeated by the blow
My first victory, reclaiming what was, is and always will be mine
alone

Like you Boudicca
I will never bend to any man again

Goddess Andraste

Joey Morris

"Hail to You
Andraste
Goddess who will not be felled
By Time or Suppression
As the Light and Dark hold their balance
We too hold our heads high
On the precipice of all our battles,
Internal and against those
Who seek to claim and destroy our Land."

Warrior in Woad Ritual Meditation –
The Spirit Marking Warrior of Andraste

After we have cast the circle, called in the trees, spoken to the Mothers of the Elements, and called out to Andraste and perhaps Boudicca also, we may wish to invoke the spirit of the Equinox through the Warrior in Woad.

This calls back to the Celtic people marking themselves with the blue ritual paint made from Woad.

To mark one's self before battle was a powerful act; you crushed herbs and dyes in a form of battle potion making, calling on the essence of these plants and the land to infuse you with their blessing, and called on the War Gods to recognise you as being 'marked' as theirs on the battle field, and 'marked' for protection and victory.

Prior to the ritual you may wish to use the following chant:

> The Warrior in Woad
> "I am her
> And she is me
> The guardian in woad
> A story screams
> Across the void
> Marked in battle lines
> I hear her scream
> Guttering
> The pitch black chord of night
> I am her
> and She is me
> There is no true divide
> I cross the ocean bruised
> And weary
> To speak at fire side
> The lightning calls
> As once it did
> The drums of war unfold
> I am Her
> And She is me
> The Warrior in Woad."

Close your eyes and visualise Andraste before you, standing on the top of a grassy hill in Ancient Briton.

You can feel the wind whipping around you, cold and bracing, with Spring rain thrashing about.

You are here to scout the land, the threat of Roman invasion and those who wish to take away your inner Sovereignty.

In this space you will not fight anyone, but you watch as the light breaks through the clouds, listening for the Land Spirits and for Andraste herself to speak to you.

Messages of Rebirth, Re-emergence, and Reclaiming the self are all of pivotal importance going forward – hear the words that are only for you. How does Andraste appear to you? What does She say?

Turn to face Her, to listen, to seek to understand.

In this process of remembering, Andraste reaches out, her fingertips rich with Woad, to paint your face and body with markings that are unique to you.

Your battle paint – reminders of your inner essence and that you can do anything you set your mind to!

As the paint swirls against your skin, see it moving and glowing with an Otherworldly energy – it is more than just paint. Feel and know that you are a part of something greater; sense that you are not defeated, you will not give up on yourself, your sovereignty. You are not alone in your birthing of a new sense of yourself.

Feel yourself grow stronger, more courageous, more connected to the Land, to the Goddess, to Yourself.

Offer your gratitude to Andraste and come back to the mundane world.

The Land remembers...

How the changing nature of Warfare has impacted the Land. For a moment, I want you to consider what affect ancient Warfare versus modern Warfare might have on the land and the Spirits of that Land.

As I have already mentioned, modern Warfare has been moved 'elsewhere' by the powers that be – in what can be described as a political, social, and economic shift to benefit the powerful. War often follows the resources, and with the current choke hold the powerful have over their own land in Europe (and the UK which is sadly no longer part of Europe), and indeed in the USA, there is little to be gained from fighting at home.

Instead, modern Warfare follows the Oil and benefits the powerful by providing an "us versus them" narrative which fuels hatred against the other.

War is as ancient as human history, as is the grasping at territory and the resources that land would provide.

To the ancient Celts, it was an intimate part of everyday life, having skirmishes with neighbouring tribes, seeking riches, land, and horses or cattle from battle.

War, such as it was, fed into their honour system, with self-worth and Sovereignty being claimed through battle.

There would be no sense to the ancient Celts in obliterating the land they wished to inhabit.

Indeed, the idea of conquering armies of ancient times salting the Earth to make it uninhabitable, which was a popular folklore motif by the Middle ages, is thought by historians to be largely fanciful. There may have been rituals involving salt that was said to 'curse' the land so that the defeated could never return and grow there, but the idea of using so much salt that the Earth would be harmed beyond repair is fairly ridiculous given the precious nature of salt, the expense, as well as the logistics surrounding the amount needed to be transported to a place to kill the Earth.

The application of toxic chemicals to the Earth in modern history, however, is one of the travesties again the planet. I have said before through my work with The Morrigan, that I view Celtic battle and the life force spilt through blood on the Earth as a kind of offering to the Goddess of War. This is tied to the sacred nature of Life force within Blood.

The idea of sacrifice we have mentioned being tied to ancient mythos still survives in pagan tradition; albeit metaphorical rather than physical.

It is also usually applied to the harvest months rather than Spring, but as we know the Celtic people performed sacrifices, both animal and human, and this was directly tied to the well-being of the Land, I find it unlikely that this was not part of their spiritual path in Spring as the new seedlings sprouted.

"The best archaeological data supporting Celtic human sacrifice is the body of the man placed in Lindow bog in the first or second century C.E. We actually have the body (well, most of it) so well preserved that scientists were able to analyze his stomach contents to discover his last meal (a partially scorched grain cake). Lindow man was almost certainly a ritual sacrifice; he was strangled, hit on the head, and had his throat cut, in quick order, then surrendered to the bog. This pattern fits the "three-fold" death referred to in medieval Irish tales. What's more, the man seems to have been of high social rank, and a willing victim." - digitalmedievalist

Once again this highlights a key lesson of War Goddesses; that there can be multiple reactions to complicated energies. War is not a pleasant business, but it condenses your life force into a single moment, bringing complete clarity – all the reasons to resist death and keep fighting.

It also shows in my mind, how the Land may have received the blood of humans as a part of the ritual aspect of Death. Warfare, to the Celts, was a part of life, and in so dying the balance between humankind and other life (the Land, the trees, the plants, the animals, etc.) was more maintained.

Overpopulation and destruction of the Earth is a modern issue. Ancient forms of Warfare maintained a balance which is no longer the case.

Instead, we have to alchemize our Warrior energy, and fight to protect the Land, whenever and how so ever we can.

This does not mean sacrificing a noble to the bogs anymore (tempting as that thought can be sometimes with the rich!) It does mean fighting those in power who see the land as something to serve their ends, which, inevitably, will be the end of the human race as well.

The Earth will outlive us. We will not survive if we keep damaging the planet this way.

I do not tell people how they should act. I think it is important to raise the issue for consideration and allow a person to find their own way.

But be it changed behaviour in ourselves, charitable donation, raising awareness... whatever we do, is echoed throughout the spiritual ecosystem.

The Land Spirits know how we are behaving, and they remember.

Andraste
Kat Shaw

Lessons From Boudicca on the Spirit to Rebel from Within

Pamela Genghini Munoz

The story of Boudicca that comes to us from 2000 years ago usually takes off just after she has hit rock bottom. Her husband has died, and rather than honor his last wishes – that half his kingdom be given to his daughters – the Roman emperor Nero, through his governor, takes it all for himself and for Rome, leaving Boudicca and her daughters with nothing to show for the loyalty that she and her husband showed Rome during their years as client king and queen of the Iceni tribe in Britain. And when she protests this wrongdoing, her daughters are raped and Boudicca herself is whipped. The rage and the betrayal Boudicca would have felt must have all but consumed her.

I can see her in my mind's eye tending to her daughters, violated and broken, while her own wounds are still raw and in need of nursing. As she lays down on her stomach so as not to open the gashes on her back from the whip, she utters a prayer to her native spirits of her British Isles and whispers to herself in her ancient Celtic tongue, "I'm gonna get them."

And get them she did, burning down Camulodunum, Londinium and Verulamium before finally being defeated in battle by the Roman legions. In giving the Romans a taste of their own medicine, Boudicca followed in the footsteps of Arminius who led the Germanic tribes against Rome in 9 CE in this very way and preceded the actions Subcomandante Marcos would take with the Zapatista movement in 1994 against their respective adversaries. This archetype of the "conformist turned rebel" is also present in some of the most epic tales ever told, in figures like Moses from the Exodus story of the Hebrews, and even the ever-adorable Cesar from *Dawn of the Planet of the Apes*. Each of these leaders prevailed against an enemy that appeared larger than life and too big to fall because they first learned the ways of their enemy and then used that knowledge against them; and Boudicca earned her place as an example of this archetype as much as any of the men. Just as the Romans had taken over sites of spiritual and political importance to the native Britons and rededicated them to Rome's emperor and the Roman pantheon, so too did she lay siege to Camulodunum, where a temple dedicated to Emperor Claudius in his divine aspect had been erected. This site had once been the seat of power of the Trinovantes, another tribe of Britons, and Boudicca's army razed the site and the temple in defiance. Just as the Roman identity was used as an inspiration to the legionnaires, so too Boudicca rallied different tribes of Britain who had previously fought each other, against their common Roman enemies. What makes Boudicca exceptional, is that she did this as a woman; and moreover, that we know about her all these centuries later.

A few months ago, I was re-watching *The Burning Times,* the second documentary in Donna Read's series on Women and Spirituality. It narrates the process through which the Roman Catholic Church criminalized folk practices and spiritual beliefs of Europe's people (and as we know, the peoples who were colonized by Europeans), and demonized women's knowledge of midwifery, herbal medicine, as well as women's social circles and their participation in public life. Recognizing that some of the numbers of women burned have been seriously questioned, the documentary nonetheless breaks down the process of a trial for witchcraft beginning with an accusation and through the different degrees of interrogation and torture culminating with the execution. Historians and authors tell of the ordeal that accused women underwent, being poked, prodded, examined, questioned, and tried oftentimes without fully understanding the process. Many times, these women were peasants from the most rural and remote places in the European countryside but were tried by educated men from the urban centers of Europe, so that even the level of formality in the language would have seemed foreign and alien to them. The methods of deduction, the legal process, and ultimately the need to retain power all worked to heavily prejudice the witch trials against the accused. After all, it was much more beneficial to the power structures of the Church and the State at the time to blame witches for droughts and disease and claim a monopoly on the lines of communication between humans and the Divine, than to admit they were powerless against forces of nature like weather and plagues. Women, and especially independent, non-conforming women, were a threat to the system of modern Patriarchy developing at the time. A few centuries ago, women like me and you, who know there is a direct line to the Divine through nature, who know that our bodies are just as sacred as our spirits and dare claim sovereignty over ourselves, would have been burned as witches.

It was not until I watched *The Burning Times* again through a lens of critical analysis, parsing out who benefited, that the stain of those medieval Courts of Inquisition on our modern legal system became clear. Suddenly I could see some of the worst aspects of that system still in play in our own system of law, and still being used against the most vulnerable in our society. The fall of the Roman Empire and the rise of the Roman Catholic Church in Europe marked the gradual but successful stripping away of women's rights under the law and of our participation in the public sphere. Midwifery and the healing arts, once a woman's practice, became a criminal act unless the practitioner had attended medical school, which in turn was closed off to women. Work in many of the artisanal trades became regulated and required membership to a guild, which again would bar women from their organizations. Women were prohibited from inheriting land and property outright and became for all purposes wards of their fathers or husbands. The oppression of women that came with the witch burnings cut into the deepest levels of society and of the support groups women had created and enjoyed up to that point. Women stopped gathering in groups, lest they be suspected of conspiring to curse their village. Women were turned against each other, finding their only chance of avoiding torture was to name other women as fellow witches. The trauma of what became known as the Witchcraze is still with us. Generations of women watched their mothers and sisters tortured and burned alive, and it imprinted this very real lesson: *There is a new power structure in place now, and you are subservient within it.* And for the better part of 1500 years the lesson has stuck. Women came to distrust and judge each other, and today many of the Patriarchy's harshest treatments of us are imparted to us by other women. THAT was why there had not been a woman rebel from within since Bouddica—because for nearly 2000 years, women were simply not allowed in.

But whereas the women killed during the Witchcraze had no advocates, no rights and no redress, there are now those of us who have pushed our way into the legal system, undertaking the task of learning the rules and swearing an oath to use that knowledge to protect people and their rights and interests against the system. I came to realize the similarities between my practice of law and my practice of witchcraft a few years ago.

Like the witches of times past, people come to see me for advice when they are in trouble and do not have the knowledge to resolve their problem themselves. Like the witches of ancient times, I have specialized skills and I understand a set of rules and a language that when used in just the right way, can help my clients achieve their goals. I may not be prescribing herbs or mixing potions in my legal practice, but in crafting an argument with just the right terminology, I am casting legal spells on behalf of my clients. Following this epiphany, I began incorporating the setting of intention into my legal practice, and I have never needed additional encouragement to light candles or incense in my office. Ever.

I have an obsessive love for the U.S. Constitution, and initially my plan was to spend my entire legal career defending the freedoms contained within the Bill of Rights. But straight out of undergraduate school I got a job working at a non-profit organization that provided legal services to immigrants. It was there that I fell in love with immigration law. And not just immigration law, but asylum law, that area of law that seeks to protect people who seek refuge against persecution or torture in other countries. Few other areas of the American legal system are structured as blatantly against the individual as are our immigration and deportation laws. Unlike criminal defendants, immigrants in removal or deportation proceedings do not have the right to an attorney paid for by the government. Unlike in criminal proceedings, the rules of evidence are rarely adhered to, the burden of proof is on the Respondent once to prove that they are eligible to be in the country once it is established that they are not citizens, and there is no obligation on the part of the government to provide you with any evidence or information in their possession that could help you prevail. Many Respondents in Immigration Court do not speak the language and are unfamiliar with our legal system, culminating in a huge disadvantage from the onset of their removal proceedings. Every client begins their case facing an uphill climb, with all of these forces bearing down on them, and only me to buffer them against the harshest consequences. I once heard an attorney at a training end the session with a call to action that "our job is to shield our client from the system, and not the system from our client," so every time I step into that legal arena, I set the intention to beat the system at its own game.

I have felt called to reflect on the liminality of the spaces I occupy because throughout my life I have been fed the narrative that I can be one thing or the other. That if we are this, we cannot be that, and I have never managed to fully be just one thing. And for so many of us who move in and out of systems within the Patriarchy in order to dismantle it, the isolation can come from those within Patriarchy as well as from the movements and causes we support. After appearing on a podcast about witchcraft and justice last year, I commented to another guest how glad I was to know there are other witchy lawyers because being a lawyer who is a witch can oftentimes feel twice as lonely, since I never feel like I completely fit in either group. These days I embrace my calling to live in the liminal, and to use that to help build a better reality. And I know I am not the only one.

The pandemic and the 2020 global movement against racial injustice have put a mirror up to the face of the system we have been living in, and so many people are realizing the ugliness of the image that is being reflected back. More and more people are casting off the lens of Patriarchy and Over-consumption and all their ugly manifestations to reclaim our humanity and our right to exist whole, and the archetype of the rebel from within was made for times like these. We can invoke Boudicca in this way, calling on her strength and her resolve to aid us as we undertake to repair our own world as she did.

Her story is not one of never being knocked down. It is a story of what you do to pick yourself up and reclaim your agency when you are. Her spirit is present in every woman who has ever suffered an injustice and has dared to utter NO MORE.

Historians have commented on how women held a near equal status in society among the Celts to include prowess in battle. So, while Boudicca might not have been considered extraordinary as a Celtic woman, she is still remarkable in the annals of our Western patriarchal society because her story managed to survive these two millennia when the chronicles of so many other women were lost or never even told. Her rallying cry – to push back even against forces that seem so much bigger than ourselves in order to preserve ourselves – can be heard through these two millennia between her time and ours. *That* is the legacy of Boudicca.

Is This the Best you Can Do?

Kay Louise Aldred

A channelled message from Boudicca.

Women. Seriously. Is this the best you can do?

Where is your NO?

Why so compliant? Why so domesticated?

Why so tamed?

Delve deep for your rage. Focus on VULVA and WOMB. GO DOWN.

Rip. Scratch. Claw. Feel and hold the urges of destruction.

Then SPEAK. Let it explosively flow from you.

Cry out for your soldiers. They've be waiting too long for your call to arms.

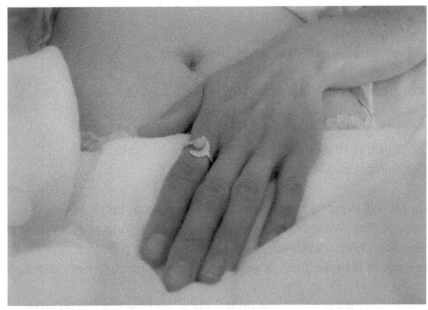

Photo by Kay Louise Aldred

Reclamation of the Broken Spirit

Joey Morris

We remember.

The lost ones, the broken ones, the hurting.

We remember the moments where we stared vacantly out into the world, feeling disconnected from it.

Our illusions shattered, the promises of a fair, safe, world dissolving at our feet.

For myself, it was a moment in the back of a car, being driven away at 3am, watching the street light blur into one another in a seemingly endless parade, each light stretching thin and eventually disappearing, a weird recollection through hazy vision.

The distinct memory of dirt on the glass, and feeling like it ought to be raining.

The rain was conspicuous by its absence.

And telling myself that life would never be the same again.

It leaves a mark somewhere, those kinds of memories, that if we are not careful, we can slip back into the state of disconnection, feeling present only in body to the world around us.

The world can be a hostile place, with an aggressive stance on conformity played in front of our eyes on a seemingly endless loop, whilst we are taught to always be ashamed.

The reclamation of self begins as we start to reject conformity; the authentic self is seeking the courage to let the world see who we are without concealment of all the idiosyncrasies peculiar to our unique blend of human.

It is the acceptance of the broken self that lends itself to reigniting the fires within ourselves.

We know what it is to feel the icy grip of despair, a cruelty that goes beyond the painful into the realm of self-abandonment; we have lost touch with the world around us for moments, leaving us an observer to the patterns of it; we study and examine from a peculiar vantage point.

It is in nature that I am reminded I can be moved by what this world has to offer.

When the atmosphere cracks in thunder and destructive elements grip the sky in a ballet of force so beyond us, or the rain rolls down a leaf in softly spoken prayer, running its length before slowly descending to the dirt beneath.

Everything seems to shift in these moments, time takes on a personality of its own, slowing everything down or racing it forward, as the crows cry out or the soul feels lifted into an endless night of stars.

Was the Witch always within me? For to see the world through 'other' eyes is surely connected to that title, for all the good that titles do.

I think perhaps it was, as I stumbled through forests as a child telling stories of ancient lands and magical spirits that others could not see.

So how does one hold onto a spark of something wondrous when all else has been forcibly removed from you, when hopelessness and violence and abuse cling to your memories like dried on gory splatter?

I tell the monsters that they do not own me.

They cannot have me; I am still here.

I will mark the world in every way I can—with honour, with truth, with beauty.

In the retelling of stories both horrifying and true, refusing to be ashamed or allow others to be so conditioned, help them to refuse to be the same as one another, to discard the notion that there is a safety in those numbers, when instead, it is handing over the power to another to dictate who you are – instead of being who you want to be, who you are shaping yourself into, honouring the magickal spark within you that cannot be silenced.

I will not be the same again.

I will be more. I will stand, time and time again, between those who seek to abuse others, and rouse the war cry of the unprotected. I will remind them they do not need to apologize for how they survived, nor be taunted by a system which shuns them or encourages their silence.

I will not be the same again.

I will embody the witch. I will reclaim my wild heritage on this earth, connected to the rolling thunderstorm and the lightning that crashes, bathe myself in the vast unconquered depths of the ocean and speak to the trees to hear their voices. I will remember the forgotten dead and the disregarded spirits to harness a live wire of power and magick.

And in the face of all who mock me, I will grin with fox fangs and raven eyes in the knowing that they cannot shame me.

I will not be the same again.

I know emptiness, and so I value connection. I know lies, and so I honour truth. I know bleakness and so I liberate my senses into a system of spiritual seeking. I know hatred and so I will pour out love from my heart. I know shame, and so I reclaim my sexuality. I stand for the broken. I stand for the lost. I stand for the hurting.

You will not have us. We will be here.

Supplication to Boudicca

Rebekah Myers

Free woman
Iceni queen
And queen of our inspiration,
Hear our call.
Through long ages of time
Your sisters call to you,
In this hour of need
We summon you.
Hear us,
Boudicca
Free woman
Iceni queen.

Every chance was given
You cooperated, negotiated
Just as we, your sisters, do –
To no avail
Their way was and is betrayal.
When word came from the west
That the sacred groves were burning,
The groans of the holy trees spiraling upward,
The curses of black-clad Druidesses paralyzing the foe –
You heard,
And cursed injustice and took up the spear.
One by one, their cities fell
And burned, and lay in smoke –
As had their promises to you; full of nothing but hot air.

Centuries have passed, at times with progression,
Of late with regression
Centuries have passed, and still, you stand
A rallying point for all who defy oppression
We are your kindred
Our daughters, raped, as yours were,
We, too, have been flogged,
Our bodies used,
Our autonomy robbed,
As you were robbed,
Our value dismissed.

Your holy rage burns yet, a living flame
Igniting our own flaming
May your fierce bravery be ours
To do that which must be done
Stand with us, Boudicca
As we stand in defiance of those
Who would suppress us yet
March with us as our ranks swell
Lead us,
Boudicca
Free woman
Iceni Queen.

Copyright © by Rebekah Myers, September 10, 2021

Boudicca Rising

Barbara O' Meara

Boudicca Speaks

Trista Hendren

As we wrap up the Medusa Speaks series,[48] I have been thinking a lot about raging Dark Goddesses. I have been contemplating all the women and Goddesses we have either never heard of—or were spoon-fed reversed patriarchal stories about. It amazes me what lengths patriarchy has gone to keep women from knowing about these archetypes—and consequently, our innate power.

I have to wonder what Boudicca's message would be to us today. What would she tell us, should she be allowed to speak?

I also have to wonder *when* women will be allowed to speak? *When* will we be finally be able to decide what to wear, how late we want to be out,[49] and what to do with our bodies? As Gail Dines wrote on Facebook:

> "We should take a lesson from the incredibly brave women in Afghanistan who are protesting in the streets against the Taliban. They could all be shot dead in the blink of an eye, and yet they refuse to back down. There should be massive protests by women all over the US in support of our sisters in Texas, in Afghanistan, and indeed all women who have to live under the patriarchy. We can't live like this!"[50]

I agree. Enough is enough!

HERstorical figures such as Boudicca are critically important now. Like Medusa, Boudicca has been demonized and blamed for her

---

48 A Girl God Books *Lessons in Lineage* online series re-storying Medusa.
49 Drake, Hannah. *"Over 400 Women Shared What They Would Do At Night If They Weren't Afraid."* WriteSomeShit.com, MAY 26, 2021.
50 Dines, Gail. Public Facebook post on September 3, 2021.

'violence.' She was a woman after all. As Sionainn McLean noted earlier, "It's almost as if women are held to a different standard."[51]

In her biography of Boudicca, Vanessa Collingridge notes:

> "This point might seem obvious but it is critical to the understanding of Boudica's place in the history books. Jenny Hall, Roman curator at the Museum of London, agrees: "The Roman army was heavily defeated by Boudica's army; now that was bad enough, but to be heavily defeated by a woman was extremely embarrassing. So, to alleviate some of that embarrassment they had to build up her story even further, making her out to be absolutely terrifying... her sex is not just a point of curiosity, it is fundamental to understanding her longevity and why she has endured the snakes-and-ladders of fame and infamy over the last two thousand years."[52]

Women are not supposed to be strong, fierce—or especially violent. And yet, most of the men we worship throughout HIStory (and I would say even the patriarchal male god) are praised for those exact qualities. God's temper tantrums are perfectly acceptable, but female rage is *not*.

We have a lot to be angry about.

Patriarchy has done a good job of suppressing that. Many women take it out on themselves via numbing through alcohol, drugs, food, shopping, or overwork—or a combination of whatever it takes to dull it all down. *Anything* is better than fury. As Adrienne Rich noted decades ago, "Most women have not even been able to touch this anger, except to drive it inward like a rusted nail."[53]

---

51 Page 116.
52 Collingridge, Vanessa. *Boudica: A Groundbreaking Biography of the True Warrior Queen*, Ebury, 2006.

It is not surprising that many women do not want to be associated with strength or rage. In females, these qualities tend to be correlated with bitches and monsters. Mona Eltahawy wrote:

> "For too long, men have called us names designed to insult, but also designed to imply we are too angry to be taken seriously: Feminazi. Ball breaker. Crazy feminist. Bitch. Hysterical. Witch. Yes, I am those things. In other words, I am an angry woman. And angry women are free women."[54]

I want to be a free woman.

In most of the world, this simply is not possible.

Violence abounds and women are targets. As Eltahawy reminds us, "Being a woman anywhere is dangerous."[55] I would add that some of us face less danger than others—which is certainly true here in Norway. It took me nearly two years to let my shoulders relax and grasp that I could safely walk the streets. I had not realized the stress that had built up in my body over the course of my life, always being on guard and on high alert. That is a heavy burden that most women carry for far too long—successfully keeping us in a cycle of fear and exhaustion both individually and collectively. As Carol P. Christ noted, it is violence or the threat of violence that allows patriarchy to continue:

> "Patriarchy is not simply the domination of women by men. Patriarchy is an integral system in which men's control of women's sexuality, private property, violence, war, and the institutions of conquest, rape, and slavery

53 Rich, Adrienne. *On Lies, Secrets, and Silence: Selected Prose 1966-1978* W. W. Norton & Company; Revised ed., 1995.

54 Eltahawy, Mona. *Headscarves and Hymens: Why the Middle East Needs a Sexual Revolution.* HarperCollins Publishers, 2015.

55 Eltahawy, Mona. *Headscarves and Hymens: Why the Middle East Needs a Sexual Revolution.* HarperCollins Publishers, 2015.

arise and thrive together. The different elements are so intertwined that it is impossible to separate one as the cause of the others. Patriarchy is an integral system of interlocking oppressions, enforced through violence."[56]

So, what can we do about this?

While I consider myself a non-violent person, I can't honestly say that I have not experienced violent rage. When my beloved friend's 12-year-old daughter was gang-raped, I wanted her rapists to choke to death on their weapons of mass destruction. That said, these 'men' were never found. So, like many of us, this is an injustice we will have to struggle with for the remainder of our lives.

And it still hurts, deeply.

My friend's daughter has become a strong and resilient young woman. But she never should have endured what she went through—nor had to struggle so hard to recover from it.

When I think about what Boudicca must have felt watching her daughters violently raped, it is almost unbearable for me. I am not sure I would have the strength to go on, yet alone to fight like she did. It must have been the strength of Andraste that carried her because her vigor and courage despite these assaults were epic.

Like a lot of mothers, thinking about my daughter being raped is not something I am able to do without a lot of painful tears. And yet, we know that most females will experience some degree of violence in their lifetimes. Many of us have been through the unthinkable.

Perhaps this is why it seems easier not to *feel* it.

---

56 Christ, Carol P. "A New Definition of Patriarchy: Control of Female Sexuality, Private Property, and War," *Feminist Theology*, March 23, 2016.

But what would a world without rape look like?

Is that something worth fighting for?

Perhaps you don't identify as a warrior, but I would say most women are warriors in their own way.

Looking back in my life, I can see many times where I needed to take on a warrior stance to protect my body, my life, or my children. Whether it was during the Rapebook campaign where I received death and rape threats[57]—or my 9 months in Family Court, where I had to defy the judge's orders to keep my children alive.

So many of our sisters are plagued with depression, mental illness, addiction, and PTSD: I would argue that most women suffer from what Dr. Valerie Rein describes as Patriarchy Stress Disorder.[58]

Many of us have had a long spiritual or physical battles the last few years with the Covid pandemic. Our dear sister Fig Ally (who I quoted at the beginning of this book) left us too soon after a lengthy struggle with long-haul Covid. At the time of this writing, my dear circle sister Camilla is also fighting for her life after a 20-year battle with Crohn's Disease. These sisters are both gentle warriors in my book.

Unfortunately, as Boudicca's life shows us, there are some battles we can't win under patriarchy. As Barbara Whiterose Marie McSweeney wrote:

> "I worry about the modern-day myth I encounter so often: the one that assures girls and women that if we are just

57 Chemaly, Soraya. "Facebook's big misogyny problem." *The Guardian*, April 18, 2013.
58 Rein, Valerie PhD. *Patriarchy Stress Disorder: The Invisible Inner Barrier to Women's Happiness and Fulfillment*. Lioncrest Publishing, 2019.

self-knowledgeable enough, determined enough, and confident enough, we will flourish and thrive. Women have always had self-knowledge, determination, and confidence, but we haven't always flourished or thrived. Boldness and defiance are not always welcomed.

Some things are stronger than us. We can be overrun by unwarranted power, by male supremacy, by a zero-sum mentality, and by our families' passive negligence or active disregard. In a woman-hating culture, spunk is not enough. Nor is a warrior spirit; some warriors lose.[59]

This is not an easy thing for me to accept.

As women, we have lost too much already. Throughout HIStory, too many women have sacrificed everything. And yet, we are still *here*.

As Kaalii Cargill asked, "What's it all been for?"[60]

I also have to ask myself, as Kay Louise Aldred did, *Is this the best we can do?*[61] Are we doing our best? In what ways are we still appeasing patriarchy, denying ourselves and our sisters?

Why aren't there Gulabi Gang's all over this rape-infested world?

As Assata Shakur wrote, "Nobody in the world, nobody in history, has ever gotten their freedom by appealing to the moral sense of the people who were oppressing them."[62]

---

59 McSweeney, Barbara Whiterose Marie PhD. "When the Warrior Doesn't Win." Warrior Queen: Answering the Call of The Morrigan. Girl God Books, 2021.
60 Page 53.
61 Page 134.
62 Shakur, Assata. *Assata: An Autobiography.* Lawrence Hill Books; 1st edition, 2001.

It is easy to taut non-violence living in relative safety, but there were times in my life when I would have had no issue with self-defense to save my own life or that of my children. When I think of the lives of my nieces and nephews in Lebanon, I am humbled to know that I am in no position to lecture much of the world on the virtues of non-violence. Najla Said's passage from her memoir has stayed with me all these years later.

> "There's something I want to explain. And I want to be clear about it. You can spend your life being a humanist, a pacifist, a thoughtful person who does not even think about hating, or does not even know what it is to hate— that is to say, you can really and truly be a human being who is tolerant and open-minded and humane, judging people by how they behave toward you, and treating them the way you wished to be treated, but when you are being attacked, when bombs are falling around you, planes are hovering over your head, when your life is in danger and you are scared, It is so easy to look up to the sky and feel abject, boiling hatred for the people doing this to you."[63]

As I watch the aftermath of the US leaving Afghanistan from the safety of my living room, I continue to ask myself, *what do we owe our Afghani sisters who have no choice now but to fight?*

What are our obligations to our daughters and sisters who face brutality, oppression, and rape—particularly when the policies of our own countries have caused much of this horror?

What do we owe ourselves in terms of healing the sadism, abuse, and rape many of us have endured?

---

63 Said, Najla. *Looking for Palestine: Growing Up Confused in an Arab-American Family.* Riverhead Books; 2014.

I think we also must become warriors of healing so that we do not continue to perpetuate the generational trauma so many of us are born into.

So, while I still dream of a world filled with flowers, love, and peace—I also know we have a long way to get there.

Unfortunately, we still live in a world that is unbearable for far too many of us.

That can't change soon enough.

May Andraste guide us on a path that honor's Boudicca's spirit— and heals the hurt patriarchy has inflicted for far too long.

List of Contributors

Andrea Redmond has been a feminist rights activist, artist, and pagan for over 50 years. She has been a devotee of The Morrigan since a young girl.

She was born on Prince Edward Island, Canada of Irish descent and moved to Ireland with her young family and there, she was one of the first women in Belfast to paint wall murals. Her first mural in 1983 honoured women rights activists from Ireland, and South Africa. She has painted over 40 murals with similar themes and her work has featured in a number of publications and films on Northern Ireland.

She has worked and chaired a number of women's, art and multicultural groups. She has taught programs in art, community development and youth work. She is a mother to three children and returned to education in her 40s, completing her PhD, at the University of Ulster.

Andrea currently, resides in rural Donegal, Ireland where she operates her art studio/workshop. Her artwork is in permanent collections and galleries in Ireland, Canada, and the United States.

Arlene Bailey is a visionary artist and author working in the realm of the Sacred Female in all her many visages. Arlene's paintings and poetry/prose reflect the raw, visceral, and sacred wild in all women, while challenging and questioning everything we know to be true about *the who* of who we are as women walking in this time.

Through her magical weavings in word and paint—and, drawing on her trainings and skills as an Ordained Priestess, Women's Mysteries Facilitator, Wise Woman Herbalist, Energy Medicine Practitioner and Retired Anthropologist—Arlene invites women to step into personal sovereignty as they listen to their ancient memories and voice of their soul.

Published in several Girl God Books' anthologies, Arlene is also a monthly contributor to *Return to Mago* E-Magazine and has writings in two forthcoming Mago anthologies. Her work can also be found on *The Sacred Wild*, a page on Facebook about re-wilding woman's soul.

Along with her partner and five cats, this Wild Crone lives on 18 acres of deep woods and quartz outcroppings in the Uwharrie Mountains of North Carolina, USA.

www.facebook.com/sacredwildstudio
www.instagram.com/arlenebaileyartist
www.magobooks.com
www.magoism.net

Barbara O'Meara published writer, co-editor of 'Soul Seers Irish Anthology of Celtic Shamanism', professional visual artist. Exhibitions include 'B.O.R.N. -Babies of Ravaged Nations', group shows Lockhart Gallery New York & 'The Drawing Box' Europe, America, Far East & 'Herstory' Brigid's of the World & Black Lives Matter. Community projects, i.e., 'Stitched With Love' Tuam Baby Blanket laid over the burial site at the Mother & Child Home, shown at KOLO International Women's Non Killing Cross Borders Summit in Sarajevo held by Bosnian women survivors. She is continually developing empowering women's 'Art as Activism' events i.e., 'Sort Our Smears' Campaign at 'Festival of Feminisms'. Collections: Microsoft, ESB, Dept Foreign Affairs, Irish Life, Impact Trade Union, Bologna District Council, Behaviour & Attitudes. Art review: "Barbara O'Meara's recent paintings dealing with home and Covid are extremely beautiful and extremely coherent in their communication. Rarely is it seen where painting is used to convey complex emotional human conditions".
www.barbaraomearaartist.com

H. Byron Ballard, BA, MFA, is a western NC native, teacher, folklorist and writer. She has served as a featured speaker and teacher at Sacred Space Conference, Summerland Spirit Festival,

Pagan Spirit Gathering, Southeast Wise Women's Herbal Conference, Glastonbury Goddess Conference, Heartland, Sirius Rising, Starwood, Scottish Pagan Federation Conference and other gatherings. She is senior priestess and co-founder of Mother Grove Goddess Temple and the Coalition of Earth Religions/CERES, both in Asheville, NC.

Her essays are featured in several anthologies and she writes a regular column for *Witches and Pagans* Magazine. Her book *Staubs and Ditchwater* debuted in 2012 and the companion volume *Asfidity and Mad-Stones* was published in Oct. 2015. *Embracing Willendorf: A Witch's Way of Loving Your Body to Health and Fitness* launched in May, 2017. *Earth Works: Ceremonies in Tower Time* debuted in June 2018. Byron is currently at work on *Gnarled Talisman: Old Wild Magics of the Motherland* and *The Ragged Wound: Tending the Soul of Appalachia*.

Claire Dorey
Goldsmiths: BA Hons Fine Art.
Main Employment: Journalist and Creative, UK and overseas.
Artist: Most notable group show: Pillow Talk at the Tate Modern. Included in the Pillow Talk Book.

Curator: 3 x grass roots SLWA exhibitions and educational events on the subject of Female Empowerment, showcasing female artists, academic speeches and local musicians. Silence Is Over – Raising awareness on violence towards women; Ex Voto – Existential Mexican Art Therapy; Heo – Female empowerment in the self-portrait.

Extra study: Suppressed Female History: History of the Goddess; Accessing Creative Wisdom; Sound and Breath Work; Reiki Master; Colour Therapy; Hand Mudras; Reflexology; Sculpture. Teaching Workshops: Sculpture and Drawing.

Emma Clark is an editor and writer working in the field of Celtic scholarship, with an MA (Hons), MSc and PhD in Celtic Studies. She teaches classes in Celtic and Gaelic at the University of Edinburgh and has published books and articles on the subject of Gaelic literature and culture. Her PhD thesis centred on the politics of landscape in modern Scottish Gaelic poetry.

Emma is a Priestess of Cerridwen in-training within the Avalonian Tradition of the Glastonbury Goddess Temple and is currently working on a book about the interconnection between the path of motherhood and the priestess path.

In her younger days, **Erika Lopp** chose a path to help others. She attended college and received a Bachelor of Arts in Sociology and later a Master's in Education and Counseling Psychology in order to help victims of domestic violence. Later, her heart led her to an Anthropology degree out of her love for history, archaeology, and cultural studies. She currently works for a cultural resource management firm called Corn Island Archaeology. Her passions include an avid love for the realm of magic, including, mythology, magical herbalism, and moon lore. Her creative soul has led her to a love for gardening, healing herbs, arts, crafts, baking, photography and writing. Things that inspire Erika: An open moonflower at dusk, the sunrise on a cool fall morning, and the distant call of the crow.

Hayley Arrington is a mythologist, poet, and writer. She received her MA in women's spirituality from the Institute of Transpersonal Psychology in Palo Alto, CA, where she wrote her thesis on Celtic sun goddesses. Her writings have appeared in various publications online and in print, including previous Girl God publications, *On the Wings of Isis* and *Inanna's Ascent*; *Whole and Holy: A Goddess Devotional*, and *SageWoman Magazine*. Her interests include mythology and folklore as sacred text, writing essays, fiction and poetry, and discovering women's myriad ways of knowing. She is a polytheist Witch and is particularly devoted to Pelasgian Hera. Hayley is from the greater Los Angeles area, where she lives with her husband and son. Learn more at her Arthurian Witch blog at loathlylady.wordpress.com.

Iris Eve is a poet, singer-songwriter, artist, tarot reader and the founder and curator of "SHE On The Tip Of Her Tongue," a popular social media site that amplifies the voices and art of women. You can find her at cunningandkeening.com

Jaclyn Cherie has her roots in Upstate New York. She is an Author, Witch, Feminist and Luciferian. The Owner and Creatrix of The Nephilim Rising strives to tell raw, real stories of Magick, the human condition, Sacred Sex, Women's Issues and her favorite topic, rebellion. Preferring the Shadows to the Light, her Magick and writing reflect this; it is in the Darkness that she found her true form. Her written works originate from the watery depths of her Cancerian Soul and chronicle her cyclical death and rebirth from the Womb of the Dragon.

Jeanne Raines is a retired massage therapist, semi-retired Mental Health Counselor, and survivor of what childhood had to throw at someone who sometimes commits art. "The Empowered Child" reflects the journey of healing in which dragons must be confronted, as well as the determination and courage that confrontation requires. After living with the teaching offered by this painting, Jeanne learned that the confronted dragon can become an ally.

Joey Morris is a Celtic Creatrix and UK-based daughter of The Morrigan. She is an author, creatrix CEO of Starry Eyed Supplies, and co-owner of the What the Flux podcast.

"To become a tempered blade of The Morrigan, one must be baptized in blood and fire. These struggles within my lifetime have led me to become a voice for the voiceless, to reach out to the broken, and to poke the shadows in others so that they might begin to heal.

Such a path is dangerous. But so are we. This is the birth of a wild witch who sees with their 'other eyes' and treads the path of edges, sharp and unusual, but filled with adventure, magick of the liminal and the in-between spaces." – Joey Morris

Within the spiritual landscape, her soul mission is to deepen the understanding of our interconnectedness by honouring the sacred and exploring the masks of the self through channelling relationships to the Divine through written work, poetry, videos, products, and services.

Kaalii Cargill is an author, artist, psychotherapist, and teacher. Her PhD explored women's reproductive autonomy through psychology, history, mythology, and anthropology: [https://trove.nla.gov.au/work/3800122 - *A Phenomenological Investigation of a Psychobiological Method of Birth Control,* 2000. Monash University]. Her non-fiction book - *Don't Take It laying Down: Life According to the Goddess* - is based on her PhD research.

Kaalii has published 7 books and co-edited two Mago Books anthologies: *She Rises: Why Goddess Feminism, Activism, and Spirituality*, Vol 1 (2015) and *She Summons: Why Goddess Feminism, Activism, and Spirituality* (2021), both with Helen Hye-Sook Hwang. Kaalii's speculative and fantasy fiction weaves themes of mythology, Wicca, and ecofeminism - https://kaalii.wixsite.com/soulstory

Kaalii is a mother and grandmother, currently living in the hills outside Melbourne, Australia, and travelling to ancient Goddess sites to "visit with the Grandmothers".

Karen Storminger has been a practicing polytheist pagan most of her life. Her interests and practices include a mix of paganism, healing practices and personal study and practice with The Morrigan, Hecate, Brigid, and most recently The Cailleach. Karen is a devotee of The Morrigan. She is an active member of the Connecticut Wiccan and Pagan Network and The Tuatha De Morrigan groups. Karen has been writing poetry of all kinds since an early age and blogs periodically at: https://thecrowandthedragonfly.wordpress.com

She has had poetry published in anthologies; *Garland of the Goddess* and *The Dark Ones* as well as other written works, including the recent Girl God publication *Warrior Queen: Answering the Call of The Morrigan*. A teacher and a healer in all aspects of her life, Karen believes that living itself is an act of devotion and walks through each day with the Goddess at her back, by her side and always in her heart.

Kathy Barenskie is labelled in the 'Medical Model' of diagnostic terms, to be an Autistic. This naive, trusting way of 'Being' has resulted in having faced many difficult experiences in her life. Yet also, it has afforded her many strengths. In reality, she has been blessed with a great empathy and sensitivity. She is a Mother of three grown-up wonderful children.

Her career path has flowed along the path of discovery of herself and being in the service of others: Registered State General Nurse, Accredited Psychodynamic Therapist, Reiki Master, Dru Yoga Teacher, Yoga Meditation Teacher, Laughter Yoga Leader. Now, in her 50s, she practices a Core Shamanism and is also a certified Shamanic Counsellor. As a special interest, Kathy crafts tools of power—Rattles, Snake Charms, Spells, Totems with Crystals and Stones.

Kat Shaw prides herself on breaking through the stereotypical views of beauty that have been cast upon society by the media, having made her name painting the glorious reality that is a woman's body.

Her nude studies of real women garnered unprecedented popularity within only a few short months, as women were crying out for themselves to be portrayed in art, rather than the airbrushed images of the perfection of the female form that are so rife in today's culture.

After graduating with a fine art degree, Kat achieved a successful full-time teaching career for 14 years, and continues to teach art part-time whilst passionately pursuing her mission of world domination by empowering as many women as possible to reach their fullest potential by embracing their bodies and loving themselves wholeheartedly.

Kat spreads her inspirational magic through her artwork, her Wellbeing business, "Fabulously Imperfect", and her dedication to Goddess energy.

Reiki is a huge part of her life, and as a Reiki Master, Kat is committed to sharing Reiki, teaching Usui, Angelic and Karuna Reiki, and channelling Reiki energy through her artwork to uplift and heal.

As a Sister of Avalon, Kat also works directly with her Goddess consciousness, connecting to Goddess and Priestess energy and translating it into Divine Feminine infused paintings to inspire women and spread Goddess love.

Kat is also a belly dancer, mum to a gorgeous teenage daughter, and an avid pioneer to improve the lives of rescue animals.

Kay Louise Aldred writes and edits for Girl God Books. She has contributed to the Girl God Anthologies *Warrior Queen, Answering the Call of the Morrigan, In Defiance of Oppression - and Just as I am - Hymns Affirming the Divine Female*. Kay will also feature in the Girl God Anthology *Songs of Solstice - Goddess*

Carols, scheduled for publication in 2022. Currently she is co-editing the four upcoming Girl God Anthologies: *Re-Membering with Goddess: Healing the Patriarchal Perpetuation of Trauma, The Crone Initiation and Invitation: Women speak on the Menopause Journey, Rainbow Goddess - Celebrating Neurodiversity* and Pain Perspectives: Finding Meaning in the Fire. Scheduled publication for these books is 2022/2023. In addition, Kay is writing her own books. *Mentorship of Goddess: Growing Sacred Womanhood* will be published June 2022 and *Making Love with the Divine: Sacred, Ecstatic, Erotic Experiences* is scheduled for February 2023. Finally, Kay and her husband Dan Aldred, are co-authoring a book together, *Embodied Education*, which will be available June 2023.

Lady Wolf is a Triple Ordained Wiccan High Priestess representing the Alexandrian/Hermetic, Eclectic and Dianic Lineage.
She is mother and Priestess of the Utah Goddess Temple. Utah's FIRST sanctioned and dedicated Temple to the Goddess.

She is a Green Witch and Master Herbalist with over 20 years of experience working with plants as sacred healing allies.

She is a Certified Hypnotherapist, Reiki Master, Crystal Therapist, Published Pagan Author, Reflexologist, Cacao Practitioner, Initiated Bard, Initiated Dianic Witch, former Coven Mother/Priestess and practicing witch with over 26 years of experience in the Craft.

Lady Wolf is dedicated to raising awareness that #witchcraftitsathing and helping educate and empower witches of all levels and degrees.

Lady Wolf is the creatrix and founder of the Desert Sage Witchcraft Tradition anchored in animism and shapeshifting through desert Magick.

Lady Wolf has trained with some of the best in the field of witchcraft from Selena Fox, Zsuzsanna Budapest, Susun Weed, Diana Paxson, Courtney Weber Hoover, Laura Tempest,

Christopher Penczak, Ellen Dugan and many more.

As an Eternal Student Lady Wolf is determined to never stop learning! She is currently enrolled in the Order of Bards, Ovates and Druids.

Lisbeth Cheever-Gessaman is the artist and illustrator of "The Divine Feminine Oracle" and "The Spellcasting Oracle." She is a scholar of the Divine Feminine, and a visionary artist who merges magick and technology with traditional mediums to create new interpretations of myth and archetype. Through her work she explores shamanic, astrological and mythological constructs to interpret the liminal worlds of the Divine Feminine, incorporating art and talisman to create a third phenomenon, or magical reality.

In honor of the Great Mother, and as personal witness, she creates all work under the pseudonym "SheWhoIsArt."
Website: www.shewhoisart.com
Facebook: www.facebook.com/shewhoisart
Instagram: shewhois

Lucy Pierce is a mother, artist and writer living in the Yarra Valley, Australia. Her work is born of dream and myth, vision and dance, song and circle, motherhood and eroticism, grief and quest. It is seeded in the places within that long for healing and for wholeness, an apprenticeship to the soul, a serenade of love and deep gratitude to that which is sought within her longing. Her art tries to give form to what is on the edge of knowing within her, an offering from the dark shadows, a fumbling for the light, a wooing of the mytho-poetic river that is woven through her being, keening for a truth, yearning towards awakening.

Maureen Owen – PCC, MDOT Transformational Coach, and Facilitator

Clients describe Maureen as insightful, committed to genuine partnership, kind, ruthlessly non-judgemental and having a remarkable ability to help others think outside their own perspective.

Maureen believes that we have a choice about how we respond and how we turn up in the world, no matter what circumstance we find ourselves in. She is devoted to supporting people to do just that whilst bringing the best of themselves forth.

Maureen has over 25 years' experience working with human dynamics. Her work is focused on supporting leaders navigate leadership challenges in the face of uncertainty.

Committed to fostering thought-provoking and creative partnerships, Maureen encourages her clients to use the challenges they face as catalysts for growth, and the opportunity to learn, bringing more of themselves and their gifts forward to expand what's possible.

Websites
www.lotusspace.com.au/
www.owenconsultingservices.com.au/

Social Media
www.linkedin.com/in/maureenowen/
https://www.facebook.com/lotusspacewisdom

Melody Bergman is a writer and art-lover living in northern Minnesota. Through creative writing and following her path, she has processed her childhood traumas and supports those she loves through their own healing journeys. Writing is an outlet of pure joy, one she can't help but indulge daily. She's been an avid writer of short fiction since childhood and is currently working on her first novel. You can find her on Instagram @melodymbergman where she posts her nature photography, collage art, and snippets of writing.

Molly Roberts is a mixed media painter, art witch and author living on the shores of Lake Michigan. Her colorful approach centers on the space where the arts and magickal traditions overlap with a focus on self-discovery and play. Over the past seven years, Molly's work has inspired burgeoning artists all over the world to create art and magick in their own lives through her YouTube channel, books and online community.

Pamela Genghini Munoz is an immigration attorney, ordained Universal Life Church clergy, and self-described eclectic witch on the U.S.-Mexico Border. She has been published in *Sage Woman Magazine*, appeared on the Missing Witches Podcast, and blogs about the intersection of feminism, spirituality, politics and the human experience at ladylawyerwitch.org. Pamela lives in El Paso, Texas with her husband, son, and a zoo that includes 7 dogs, 2 turtles, 1 snake, 1 cat and countless fresh and saltwater creatures. You can follow her on Instagram @lawyerwitchpam

Pandora Le Cora is a long-time practicing witch, mental health peer worker, support carer and married mother of two residing on Bayali land in so-called Queensland, Australia. In her spare time, she can be found spending time with her family, drawing, painting, dancing, reading, gardening, drinking tea, writing and sporadically vlogging and blogging. This essay is her first submission for an anthology.

Pat Daly (editor) is a mother of three daughters and proud grandma. A published author / writer on career and job search issues, Pat lives in Portland, Oregon. She has edited each and every Girl God book from the beginning.

Rebekah Myers is dedicated to opening doors of understanding on behalf of women everywhere. She is the founder/facilitator of Sacred Sisters Full Moon Circle, which serves as a virtual Facebook and Instagram public page, a private Facebook group for women, and an actual women's circle that meets in-person. For International Women's Day in March of 2018, Rebekah honored to have been one of five women recognized by KSL as Utah's most inspirational women.

Through her social anthropologist parents, Rebekah spent memorable time with the Iroquois (a matrilineal people) of Six Nations Reserve in Ontario, Canada. This experience significantly informed her life for the good. Rebekah has had a life-long interest in and passion for folklore, mythology, and ancient history, and has spent significant time in these worlds. Although Rebekah formally came later in life to women's spirituality, she has found such fulfillment on this path, that there is no turning back. As a writer, teacher, director, award-winning singer/performer/actress, mother, grandmother, and wedding officiator, Rebekah works to empower, enlighten, and uplift women and their brothers. She knows it is possible to heal the wounds of patriarchy and live with depth, meaning, and joy.

Sharon Smith is a writer, ghost writer, editor, and proofreader with a passion for helping women reconnect with their Authentic Selves and Voices. She loves and honors the Great Mother in all Her many forms and has a deep connection to Nature. She identifies as a Green Witch and follows an eclectic spiritual path that is a blending of Native American and Celtic Teachings, both in her ancestral line.

Sionainn McLean is a polytheist fire witch, on a crazy spiritual journey over the last 25 years. She has worked with The Morrigan for 5+ years. She is currently studying to get her certificate in Community Ministry, as well as a Spiritual Direction certificate with Cherry Hill Seminary. She is also studying magic and shamanistic practice with Three Worlds, One Heart School of Mystery. She's also a mom, wife, writer, and gardener.

Tamara Albanna has always been connected to the Goddess, even when she didn't realize it. As a Doula and Childbirth Educator, she witnessed divinity first hand through other women. Now as a writer, artist, Reiki healer and Tarot reader, she hopes to help others overcome their difficult pasts while healing with the Divine Mother. She has published two books on *Inanna*—*Inanna's Ascent: Reclaiming Female Power* (co-edited with Trista Hendren and Pat Daly) and *My Name is Inanna;* two books on Willendorf—*Willendorf's Legacy: The Sacred Body* (co-edited with Trista Hendren and Pat Daly) and *My Name is Goddess of Willendorf*—as well as three poetry chapbooks, *As I Lay By the Tigris and Weep, Rosewater,* and *Kismet*. Tamara currently resides in Europe with her family. She can be found at https://tamara-albanna.com

Trista Hendren founded Girl God Books in 2011 to support a necessary unraveling of the patriarchal world view of divinity. Her first book—*The Girl God*, a children's picture book—was a response to her own daughter's inability to see herself reflected in God. Since then, she has published more than 40 books by a dozen women from across the globe with help from her family and friends. Originally from Portland, Oregon, she lives in Bergen, Norway. You can learn more about her projects at www.thegirlgod.com.

Victoria Wilson-Randall lives in Plymouth with her husband Tim, and two cats: magic and midnight. She is an eclectic pagan walking a Celtic path who loves being immersed in both the online and offline pagan community. Victoria is disabled and uses mobility aids. She spends time advocating for more accessible spaces and more understanding around living with chronic pain.

Writing and creating art are her primary passions. She writes often on her blog (rosebudsandravens.com) Her dream is to run a small business selling items that she crafted and to finally write the novel that's been rattling around her brain for the last decade.

Trista's Acknowledgments

I would like to acknowledge my mother, **Pat Daly,** who has edited each and every one of my books. There would be no Girl God Books without her enormous contributions.

I was honored to work with **Joey Morris** on this project—who inspired my interest in Boudicca.

Tremendous gratitude to **Molly Roberts** for allowing us to feature her gorgeous painting as the cover art.

Many thanks to **Jaclyn Cherie** for taking time out of her busy schedule to write the beautiful Preface to this anthology.

Enormous appreciation to my husband **Anders Løberg**, who designed the book cover, prepared the document for printing and helped with website updates. Your love, support and many contributions made this book possible.

My mom and I would also like to acknowledge her wonderful partner, **Rick Weiss,** for being an all-around awesome guy—and helping us with the page numbers.

Lastly, I would like to thank my dear sisters **Tamara Albanna, Susan Morgaine, Jeanette Bjørnsen, Camilla Berge Wolff, Sharon Smith, Arlene Bailey, Tammy Nedrebø-Skurtveit, Kay Louise Aldred** and **Alyscia Cunningham** for always being right there to cheer me on in the spirit of true sisterhood.

Thank you to all our readers and Girl God supporters over the years. We love and appreciate you!

Joey's Acknowledgments

I would like to thank Molly and Victoria with much gratitude and honour. These Women have made lasting impact and continue to do so, changing the course of my life. I dedicate this anthology to them in the spirit of Women marching together to the best of their hearts.

If you enjoyed this book, please consider writing a brief review on Amazon and/or Goodreads.

What's Next?!

My Name is Boudicca by Joey Morris

Re-Membering with Goddess: Healing the Patriarchal Perpetuation of Trauma – Edited by Kay Louise Aldred, Trista Hendren and Pat Daly

The Crone Initiation and Invitation: Women speak on the Menopause Journey – Edited by Kay Louise Aldred, Trista Hendren and Pat Daly

Mentorship with Goddess: Growing Sacred Womanhood – Written by Kay Louise Aldred

Rainbow Goddess – Celebrating Neurodiversity – Edited by Kay Louise Aldred, Trista Hendren and Tamara Albanna

Making Love with the Divine: Sacred, Ecstatic, Erotic Experiences – Kay Louise Aldred

Pain Perspectives: Finding Meaning in the Fire – Edited by Kay Louise Aldred, Trista Hendren and Pat Daly

Embodied Education – Kay Louise Aldred and Dan Aldred

Changing history to HerStory – Art and Words by Kat Shaw

Just as I Am: Hymns Affirming the Divine Female – Edited by Trista Hendren, Sharon Smith and Pat Daly

Songs of Solstice: Goddess Carols – Edited by Trista Hendren, Sharon Smith and Pat Daly

Goddess Chants and Songs Book – Edited by Trista Hendren, Anique Radiant Heart and Pat Daly

Anthologies and children's books on the Black Madonna, Mary Magdalene, Mother Mary, Aradia, Kali, Brigid, Sophia, Spider Woman, Persephone and Hecate are also in the works.

The most up-to-date list can always be found at http://thegirlgod.com/publishing.php

Printed in the USA
CPSIA information can be obtained
at www.ICGtesting.com
LVHW010748230124
768658LV00017B/1295